OLD DYKES
I HAVE KNOWN

A History of the North Level
Part of the Great Level of the Fens

Arridet aridum

By P.R. Charnley

This book is

Nº: *452/1000*

of a Limited Edition of 1,000

ISBN 0 948204 51 6

Published by:
Barny Books & P.R. Charnley

Printed & Produced by:
TUCANN*design&print* • 19 High Street • Heighington • Lincoln LN4 1RG
Telephone & Fax: (01522) 790009

BURALL Limited

It is fitting that Buralls have supported the publication of this historical account of the drainage of that part of the Fens adjacent to Wisbech.

Chairman David Burall's great grandfather, Thomas, came of a well-known Cornish engineering family. As a young man he travelled to the Wisbech district to install some of the earliest Cornish beam pumping engines designed to drain the Fens. Thomas and his wife returned in later years to Waldersea, a small hamlet between Wisbech and Guyhirn, where he was the Resident Engineer to the Waldersea commissioners at the pumping station until his death in 1883.

Thomas and Catherine Burall had six children. The eldest, Thomas Tank Burall, was manager at Charles Burrell & Son, eminent agricultural engineers of Thetford, where he developed the compound steam traction engine.

A younger son, William Tank Burall, started a wholesale grocery business in Wisbech in about 1870 and was joined by his younger brother Henry Charles in 1880.

The two brothers became the founding fathers of Burall Brothers printers in 1892 after they developed and patented a quick-fix hook-on address label.

One hundred years later, Buralls has blossomed into a family of eight operating companies in the information, specialised print and publishing business.

List of Contributors

James Allan	Farmer	of	Thorney
Richard Allen	Chartered Surveyor	of	Wisbech
Dame Elizabeth Anson	Vice President ADA	of	Farnham, Surrey
Peter Allitt	Farmer	of	Gorefield
James Ashton	Farmer	of	Sutton St Edmund
J W E Banks	Farmer	of	Crowland
Geoff Beel	River Engineer	of	March
Pip Barrett	Consultant in Aquatic Plants	of	Oxford
Rt Hon Baroness Blatch CBE	Government Minister	of	Spaldwick
Ken Blow	IDB Superintendent	of	Thornton-Le-Fen, Lincs
Peter Borrows	Flood Defence Manager	of	Reading
Eric Bowles	IDB Clerk/Surveyor	of	Saxton, Yorks
N P Bradshaw	Farmer	of	Newborough
C J Brown B.V.Sc,M.R.C.V.S	Veterinary Surgeon	of	Wisbech
John F Buck	Chartered Accountant	of	Wisbech
E A Burton	Ex Chairman Middle Level 76to81	of	Benwick
John Carney	Agricultural Merchant	of	Murrow
Richard Carney	Essential Oil Producer	of	Wisbech
Dr Peter Cave	Med Practioner Rtd	of	Wisbech
T G Cave	LD Engineer	of	March
Leonard T Chase	Chairman R.L.I.D.B	of	Leominster
Denzil Chester	Customs Officer Rtd	of	Emneth
John Clarke	Farmer	of	Wisbech St Mary
Kenneth V Clarke	Highway Engineer Rtd	of	Halstead, Essex
A C Coates	Farmers	of	Gorefield
David A H Coates	Farmer	of	Sutton St Edmunds
David Coles	Farmer	of	Thorney
Graham Collier	Horticulturist	of	Wisbech
Stuart Darby	Area Manager E.A	of	Wallingford, Oxon
A G Darby	Farmer	of	Newborough
Barry E A Diggle	Chairman FDC	of	Wisbech
David Dobson	Director	of	March
Malcolm Duplock	Civil Enginner	of	Thrapston, Northants
Glyn Edwards	Director	of	Wisbech
C J Elkington	I.D.B Clerk	of	Washingborough, Lincs
N S Elgood	Brewer	of	Wisbech
Dennis Fenn	L D Engineer	of	Nassington
Gerard Fletcher	Optical Technician	of	Walepole St Peter
E R Frances	Farmer	of	Murrow
Alan Gardner	Civil Engineer	of	Doncaster
Arthur E Gee	Farmer	of	Thorney
C S Gent	Farmer	of	Sutton St Edmunds
Tony Goode	Director	of	Wisbech
Tony Goodge	L D Engineer	of	Ely
J Mervyn Green	Printer	of	Wisbech
Peter Halsey	Gentleman	of	Colyton, Devon
J M Hammond	Civil Engineer	of	Boston, Lincs
Geoff Harper	Director	of	Wisbech
S Harris	Farmer	of	Borough Fen
I W Hart	Flood Defence Engineer	of	Diss, Norfolk
Richard Hartland-Rowe	Zoologist Rtd	of	Wisbech
Vic Harris	Computer Engineer	of	Walpole St Andrew

D B Hastings	Plant Superintendent RYD	of	Barnwell
N G Harvie	Solicitor	of	Oxford
Graham Harwin	Gentleman	of	Outwell
Carl D Haynes	Gentleman	of	Spladwick, Hunts
R Heading	Farmer	of	Thorney
Arnold Hemmant	Farmer	of	Thorney
S M Hemmings	L D Engineer	of	Boston
Alan Hendrick	Consultant	of	Shenfield, Essex
Nick Hendrick	Tree Surgeon	of	Shenfield, Essex
Richard Hillier	Gentleman	of	Peterborough
R H Hinton	TDB Clerk	o	Whittlesey
N G Hobday	Gentleman	of	Wisbech
Keith Holmes	Carpet Retailer	of	Wisbech
John Honnor	L D Engineer	of	Holbeach, Lincs
Malcolm Howell	L D Engineer Rtd	of	Wells-Next-The-Sea
L G Howells	L D Enginner	of	Oldbury, Glous
J H R Hoyles	Farmer - Chairman NLIDB	of	Newton
R F Hunt-Pain	Farmer	of	Whittleswy
Ernest Hurn	Farmer	of	Thorney
Dorothy Husband	Librarian	of	Thorney
M Jeffries	Liasion Officer	of	Hingham, Norfolk
Brenda Johnson	Lecturer	of	Upwell
Tony Johnson	Lecturer Rtd	of	Wisbech
DRM Kay	TDB Clerk	of	York
Dr G L Kennedy	Med Practitoner Rtd	of	Wisbech
Roger Kilham	Farmer	of	Thorney
W R Knowles	Solicitor Rtd	of	Walpole St Andrew
Anthony F Lackner	TDB Clerk Rtd	of	Dymchurch, Kent
Steve & Sharon Lake	Computer Engineer & Carer	of	Dereham, Norfolk
Tom Lane	Farmer	of	Thorney
Dr John Lines	Med Practioner	of	Wisbech
Patrick J Lloyd	Local Correspondent	of	Kings Lynn
N S Manser	Farmer	of	Crowland
John Martin	Farmer	of	Waterbeach
Barrie A Maxwell	Civil Engineer	of	Sevenoaks, Kent
Neil McLean	Police Constable	of	Wisbech
Frank Metson	Surveyor Rtd	of	Holt, Norfolk
Stephen Morris	LD Engineer	of	Sutton St Edmunds
Malcolm Moss	MP	of	Wisbech
J H M Norris	Environment Agency Board	of	Brentwood, Essex
Rev Peter Owen-Jones	Curate	of	Wisbech St Mary
Antony Pembertson	Farmer	of	Thorney
J Pettifor	Civil Engineer	of	Eltisley
L W Pooley	Artist	of	Wisbech St Mary
John D Porter	Farmer, Chairman Witham Third I.D.B	of	Tattershall, Lincs
Roger & Kath Powell	Historian & linguist	of	Wisbech
Dan Powell	TDB Clerk	of	Oswestry, Shrops
The Lord De-Ramsey	Farmer	of	Abbots Ripton
W J Randall	Electrical Engineer	of	Elm
George Richardson	Farmer Rtd	of	Walsoken
D J Riddington	Farmer	of	Newborough
G M Riddington	Farmer	of	Crowland
Phyllis Ritchie	Farmer	of	Thorney
William S Rollings	Headmaster Rtd	of	North Walsham, Norfolk

Dr Nicolas Rosier	Gen Practitoner	of	Wisbech
J L Roughton, CBE, JP, DL, FRAgS	Farmer	of	Alford, Lincs
Alan D Salmon	Chartered Accountant	of	Wisbech
Edward Sandall	Fruit Grower	of	Wisbech
Rev R C Sanders	Baptist Pastor	of	Deeping St James
Barrie Shearer	Civil Enginner	of	Boston, Lincs
M A Siddy	I.D.B Clerk	of	Carrington, Notts
Roger Shippey	Fruit Farmer	of	Newton
J G Smedley	Gentleman	of	Wisbech
Dr Eric T Somerville	Med Practioner	of	Wisbech
F R Stovell	Agronomist	of	Ashton, Cornwall
T Stevenson	Gentleman	of	Thorney
Peter Stott	Learning Facilitator	of	Whitewell, Leics
John Taynton-Evans	IDB Clerk	of	Newport, Gwent
Maurice Tennant	Antiquary	of	Holbeach, Lincs
John O'Toole	Writer	of	Earby, Lancs
J W Tuck	Building Contractor	of	Wisbech
Joe Waltham	Farmer	of	Four Gotes
Andrew Ward	Computer Engineer	of	Guyhirn
G T Ward	Farmer	of	Gorefield
Roy Wedley	Accountant	of	Longthorpe
Myrna Whittam	Secretary	of	Thorney
K A Winfield-Chisslett	School Teacher Rtd	of	Peterborough
Peter Wood	Propogator	of	Gorefield
Tony Worth	Farmer	of	Holbeach Hurn, Lincs
Geoffrey H Wright	Coldstore Manager	of	Wisbech
John Wright	Chartered Surveyor	of	Woburn Sands
Tom Youdan	L D Engineer	of	Market Harborugh, Leics

Organisations

Association of Drainage Authorities	of	Huntingdon
Ayscouhfee Hall Museum	of	Spalding
Barton Plant LTD	of	Kettering
The Beckett Group	of	Bury St Edmunds
Clearway Products Ltd	of	Wisbech St mary
Central Library	of	Peterborough
Littlechild & Son Ltd	of	Leverington
North Level IDB	of	Thorney
David Mobile & Associates	of	Huntingdon
J M Newling & Son Ltd	of	Wisbech
James Sutton Farming Co	of	Thorney
Tween Bridge IDB	of	Thorne, Yorks
Upper Witham IDB	of	Lincoln
Environment Agency	of	Peterborough
E Coward Ltd	of	Thorney
Environment Agency (Anglian Region)	of	Peterborough
Grantham, Brundell & Farran	of	Doncaster, Yorks
C Horrell Ltd	of	Thorney

Old Dykes I Have Known

INDEX

ON THE LOCK GATES
AT EARITH

"A Sea of land, far reaching to the sky,
Long dykes, whose mist at even dims the air.
Tall reeds and waving grass, the lonesome lair
Whence startled coot and duck and moorhen fly.
The plovers' call, the herons' plaintive cry,
Break the soft stillness born of nature's prayer
Till birds and reeds and stream all seem to share
The calm in which the rushes scarcely sigh.
O lone Fenland, where silent nature sleeps
As through they meads the sluggish river creeps,
Edged by the blue forget-me-not, towards the sea.
They who best know thee, know thy bosom keeps
Deep stored, great lessons all may learn of thee,
O dim weird land, enwrapped in mystery."

T. F. Fullard

ACKNOWLEDGEMENTS

The fact that this publication ever saw the light of day is entirely due to the encouragement of *Roger and Pamela Shippey with Johnny Liz Clarke,* who in a moment of weakness agreed to interpret my scribbles and produce the first document.

My sincere thanks to *Paul* and *Nicki Land*: Paul who spent so much time producing maps.
Annette Penny who produced the final manuscript, oft under difficult circumstances.
To all the staff of the *North Level Drainage Board* for their considerable help and copious cups of coffee.
I am deeply indebted to *Edward Storey* for his time and advice. I asked him to write a foreword which became an introduction.
My thanks to *John Honnor,* Welland and Deeping Drainage Board, for his help with the glossary and use of his photographs.
To my dear *wife*, my thanks for long suffering support.

INTRODUCTION

By A Fen Author
Edward Storey

This really is a **tour de force** and there are times when the author leaves his reader breathless as his enthusiastic narrative sweeps like a March wind across the vast landscape of the Fens.

It would be true to say that we have three books in one - an autobiography, a history of the Fens, and a meticulously researched volume on fen drainage, by a man who clearly loves both nature and machines.

There are facts, statistics and dates in abundance, but they are presented against a dramatic tapestry of events, opinions and humour. If anyone thinks that a subject like drainage is doomed to be dull and clay-footed then this book will soon contradict that assumption. Arguments in committees, squabbles with the Government, conflicts over drainage rates, lost Minute Books, and the disheartening experience of knowing that, in the end, Nature still has the last word, keep this story moving at the speed of a champion fenland skater. Peter Charnley is sometimes Devil's Advocate, sometimes wilfully argumentative, and always well informed with the knowledge of his own experience.

The first chapter is intentionally light-hearted and personal as he establishes his reasons for being in the Fens and why they have kept him here for so long - which, for such an adventurer, is quite an achievement. But then, the Fens have always needed Adventurers of one sort or another and the author required that kind of spirit to take on the natives in the first place, as Cornelius Vermuyden discovered in the seventeenth century.

For a man who has such a natural love of the sea - Peter was in the Royal Navy and also qualified as a diver - it was inevitable that one day he would find himself working in the 'waterlands' of Cambridgeshire, continuing the essential work begun by all those fen-drainers before him.

I particularly enjoyed his chapter on the Norman occupation which gives us some idea of how few people then lived in the Fens:

'The Doomsday Inquest of AD 1087 showed the North Level area to be very sparsely populated with only five people and less than two oxen per thousand acres..... The Hundred was an administrative area between the village and the shire..... and is thought to have been an area of one hundred hides; a hide being an area which would support one peasant family.....'

We also learn how this country came to have its famous shire horses:

'Most of the Norman war horses were bred in the marshlands of Holland, Belgium and Germany, their large feet being able to support, not only their own weight, but also that of a fully armoured knight.... William of Normandy had defeated the English by use of the heavy horse, importing both Flemish and Dutch stallions to develop the required attributes..... Selective breeding resulted in the slowest and heaviest being bred in the Fens; so huge were these animals and so large their feet that they became unsuitable as war horses, but very useful as draught animals.... So successful had become the breeding of Great Horses here that, by the advent of the War of the Roses, the export of the finest had started, first to nearby European countries and, later, to as far away as Italy.....'

Understandably his chapters on fen drainage, particularly from the seventeenth century on, are well-informed and I was pleased to read that the author thinks that, as far as Cornelius Vermuyden is concerned "it is inconceivable and utterly shameful that a lasting monument to his genius as a great, if not the greatest 17th century engineer, has not been erected in the Fenland he ventured to drain". Instead he was left to die a penniless, lonely old man in London, forgotten by the high tide of history that was then sweeping across England with the Restoration of the Monarchy.

But the Dutchman's work was to continue and we are reminded in this story by Peter Charnley that "The Laws and Customs of Drainage are the most ancient in the kingdom."

Despite all the efforts and ingenuity of Man to keep the Fens drained, Nature can still demonstrate her superiority in the most awesome ways, as the severe floods of this century alone have shown. The floods of 1947 especially have established their place in our history as some of the most dramatic inundations for a thousand years. The whole of Fenland was affected and each farm and village has its own drama to tell. No wonder the Fenmen refer to the event as "The Second Flood", believing that only Noah could have known anything worse. That was the year when "a shoal of dolphins, 6 - 8 ft. long, came up the River Nene as far as the Dog-in-a-Doublet sluice. It was reported that most of them were destroyed by shooting. Perhaps we are more enlightened these days." I wonder.

There are many more such incidents and countless anecdotes to enrich this volume about a part of England that **is** different from anywhere else. It is the most man-made landscape in the British Isles yet steeped in traditions that go back to prehistoric times.

My last quote must be one to illustrate the effect that the new powerful drainage pumps had on the lives of the people who lived close to them:

'A Board member, whose home was some two hundred yards away from the new Dog-in-a-Doublet pump and behind a bank, asked me to go and see him when the pumps were working. I could hear a high-pitched whine outside his house, louder than it was near the pumps, though not uncomfortably so. He took me into the house, gave me a large whisky and said "sit there for a few minutes." We sat chatting for about fifteen minutes, then suddenly his collection of cut-glass in a glass-fronted cabinet, sprang into life, chattering, clinking and singing so loudly you could hardly hear yourself speak. We took some of the glasses out of the cabinet and made sure none were touching, but it made no difference. When the sound-consultant heard it he was amazed but managed to track it down to a wave-length against which the pump was finally shrouded. End of problem - £1,200 later...."

As the author says, there is never a dull moment in the Fens and you need to belong to a rare and special race of folk to survive. In this absorbing book he has made sure that we do not forget what some of those essential qualities are.

Edward Storey
© 1994

CHAPTER I

Musings and Memories

Sitting at my window watching the tide flow up along the murky, unlovely River Nene at Wisbech, I realised what a wondrous tale this ancient river could tell.

Usually active, but forced to sit about for hours, after self-inflicted damage on the golf course - I found tide watching very conducive to reflecting on the past, what was, and what might have been. Having struggled to my local hostelry, the Rose Tavern, however, and been plied with copious quantities of ale, my friends suggested, "Write a book." I staggered home, slightly inebriated, but euphoric, and started work immediately before the urge wore off.

The decision made, there was no turning back. The History of the North Level, etc. by an Engineer, was born, and I became absorbed in the manifold achievements including, my own small contribution, which had resulted in this area becoming both 'The Garden' and 'Bread Basket' of England.

Having spent many happy hours as a small boy making dams, building banks and watching them breached by water, I progressed to broader water with boats and rafts. Fascinating stuff, water. Evacuated to a school by the sea when the Second World War started, I was engrossed in the wonders of this immense ocean kingdom: the flow of the tides over the sand, the natural and man-made protection from the ravages of the waves, the thrill of controlling a very small boat in what appeared to me to be a hurricane with thirty-foot waves, being swept ashore, recovering the boat and the broken bits while experiencing the strength and power of wind-blown breaking waves.

My father showed no surprise when he learned that I had volunteered for Navy training at 17 and had been accepted into the then 'Y' scheme. Being 4' 10" and weighing a mere eight stone, a uniform had to be made specially; my voice hadn't broken, which was embarrassing, particularly in the wartime Navy. Fortunately my father's RAF Physical Training Instructor had coached me well in unarmed combat, with some knowledge of pressure points I was able to repel boarders!

I remember a Three Badge Chief Signalman, who, after my first squeaky-voiced parade, called me to his caboosh and gave me my first taste of 'neaters', (straight navy rum), with the comment. "This'll make a man of you, son..." Every day, for three weeks, Jack shared his rum ration with me.

Despite, or perhaps because of the 'neaters', one day, whilst drilling a squad of 108 sailors, on calling the order "Slope Arms", it came out as a high-pitched "Slope!..." and a croaky, deep "....ARMS!"

Such was the esprit de corps that they all dropped their rifles and cheered - and what a party it was that night!

Having opted to go for a commission, some nameless 'two-ringer', (lieutenant), offered the advice, "As a short-arse you have to push yourself forward at every opportunity!" which resulted in my volunteering for anything and everything, eventually being commissioned as a Midshipman, the lowest of the low, in the RNVR, (Royal Navy Volunteer Reserve), a mere five of us passing out of the original draft of 109.

There followed some delightful, horrific, interesting and rewarding years; which, doubtless helped to mould my attitude - which still remains - that 'Good things are often wrapped in small parcels!'

I became a qualified diver, semi-expert in marine salvage, and a reasonable helmsman. I returned to my parents, a penniless tearaway, vaguely intending pursuing an out-door occupation. Finally, my father, by now retired, sent me to the great E. L. Kelting, Engineer to the Somerset Catchment Board, to whom I was assigned as 'Civil Engineering Assistant under Agreement': the start of my days in Land Drainage. I look back on those days with nostalgia. We ex-Servicemen lived life to the full, worked exceedingly hard, and played even harder enabling me to gain a qualification to Wimbledon and a county Rugby trial, as well as completing several original river schemes which still survive.

Practical joking in the drawing office was rife. Everybody received the 'treatment' - dreamed up by the ex-Servicemen among us. One very serious young man, not ex-service, doing a drawing, fell victim to a swinging lamp which I had rigged with a length of black cotton. "Hell of a draught in here," he grumbled, inspecting the windows. Then he shut the door, but noticed the cotton. He was not amused and went to complain about disruption to his work. Waiting apprehensively, we heard a loud guffaw. "Please, Mr Hitchen, the boys are teasing me!" We chorused, when he reappeared, flushed crimson, and disappeared for the rest of the day. However, he returned next morning, sadder and wiser.

One engineer always wore a trilby which he left on his desk instead of hanging it up. That hat suffered abominably: belted across the office, turned inside out, sometimes accompanying its owner with a large notice pinned to the back saying "Press". One day, approaching the office, I was told, "Bill's left his hat on the table again." "Right! I'll deal with it." On entering, I belted the hat across the room with an almighty swipe saying, "Hang up your blooming hat, Bill!" Then I realised it was a grey Homburg, and the Solicitor's Clerk was staring at me horrified. Retrieving the hat and brushing it down, I returned it to the owner with apologies, feeling extremely foolish. Whenever the little man came into the office after that, he clutched his precious Homburg to his chest.

Sadly, practical jokes do not seem as popular these days, yet being able to laugh at oneself is a superb character builder.

We undertook a variety of tasks, from selecting 30 foot long elms for felling, trimming, hauling-out and driving by hand operated piling frame into the River Parrett bank, to towing cattle from the flood waters with a rowing boat; learning how to pole-vault rhynes, (ditches), to pacifying irate farmers whose land was underwater because the banks had been overtopped. We learned much from the River Foremen, who knew how to do everything, if not necessarily *why*, but would willingly try anything. Where are they now?

I enjoyed a small triumph in Somerset. In summer, the rivers and outfalls there silt up - even more than on the East Coast - and clearing them before the winter rain is a problem. The Huntspill River, (cut during World War II to drain the Brue Marshes and provide cooling water storage to the Royal Armaments Factory), because of its size and scantry summer flow, silted badly, I proposed cleaning three-quarter-mile gut with one big explosion, letting go the sluices at the same time. Mr. Kelting agreed and contacted Johnson, the Engineer to the Ministry, for grant aid. He was only willing to approve the grant *if* it worked and with the proviso that all Johnson's Regional Engineers should observe the procedure and effect in case something was proposed in their area, Kelting promptly put my job on the line.

Over the next few weeks we put two-pound water-proof charges every 10 feet along the three-quarter mile gut at a depth of 4 feet, and I connected them all up with Cordex, provided though my contact with chums in Marine Salvage at Rosythe.

On the day, low water was at noon, the river was full and the sluice manned. The men from the Ministry all seemed to be dressed alike, with curly-brimmed brown trilbies and shorty white macs - Johnson himself, however, wore three-quarter rubber boots and a long oilskin.

We marched down the bank of the outfall to where the electric charger was placed. The wind was at our backs at ground level, an oversight on my part.

At last the order to 'go' came from Kelting, and three-quarters of a mile of sluice gut bed was seen to rise - seemingly slowly - into the air; the sluices opened, the water gushed down with a mighty roar.

Alas, some 200 feet above the ground the wind was blowing in the opposite direction and suddenly, this vast cloud of silt, which blotted out the sun, started drifting back!

"Hold fast!" I yelled , "It will go over us!"

Only Kelting and Johnson believed me; the rest of the trilby and mac brigade took off in their borrowed wellies away from the avenging cloud. Gravity inexorably took its toll, all the white macs were caught in the silt's downward path! Some ministry men fell into rills in saltings, others lost their wellies, all became muddy, brown, curly hat brims full of silt.

The operation proved to be highly successful and I was congratulated by Kelting and Johnson - albeit with wry grins! We got our grant and I kept my job. But I was reminded of the occasion by the Ministry engineers for quite a while. They were not amused, I can't think why. After all we had lent them the wellies!

In 1947, Allermoor - bounded by the River Parrett banks - was flooded, almost to the top of the bank alongside Kings' Sedgemoor and we patrolled the bank all night armed with shot-guns in an attempt to prevent man-made breaches: pointlessly, I might add, as Sedgemoor flooded the next day through two breaches. Some time later, we improved the channel through Allermoor and Kings' Sedgemoor, to cater for flood-water, constructing the bridge parapets 3 feet thick with sluices on the up-stream face, winding gear could only be reached through 1 inch thick steel doors on the roadward side, special long handles were kept in the office to prevent unlawful use. Another new channel has since been constructed to control the flood discharge, but the old edifice is still employed.

My income was insufficient for my desired lifestyle, it was time to move. I became District Engineer for the Malton area of North Yorkshire - upland stuff!

The York office was even worse than my Somerset starting point: 8 engineers cramped in a room 22 feet by 16. On the back of the door, however, hung a dartboard. Lunchtime darts were compulsory for us all, from the Divisional Engineer, Philip Leach, to the humblest trainee - and for money! I became quite proficient! Again, we worked hard and played hard, had lots of fun and laughter and I got familiar with many facets of Upland river engineering, including the purchase of land from farmers for river and embankment improvements in the good old-fashioned way, in the pub, until both parties were satisfied - internally and financially. No signature! just a handshake. Next day to Leeds, then back to the farmer with the Deed of Sale and purchase money. Much cheaper than going through the present rigmarole, agents and all. Perhaps in the balmy days of 1951 everyone was honest!

One of the benefits of these interesting years was an involvement in the trout hatchery, also with the barge traffic hauling stone for pitching the tidal banks: all direct labour and not a contract in sight. At one stage we had 150 men laying stone, all dressed and caulked, a highly skilled job. Maintenance and weed-cutting in the trout steams was carried out carefully by hand, everyone knowing what and what not to cut, how to produce the right runs and how to stake-in hawthorn on the eroding banks to prevent under-cutting, leaving the cliffs for the sand-martins and kingfishers. Modern 'green' conservationists did not invent the idea. For us, conservation was preserving the status quo, practiced for centuries and part of life.

Sport was still a big interest. Rugby, another county trial; darts, (but only for the money!); poaching, highly mechanised and successful aided by a telescopic .22 rifle. I was an expert shot, shooting for King Edward VII at Bisley on three occasions, winning on one! There was also a season playing mid-week Rugby League for York, under the alias Peter Read. Very illicit of course, but it added to the coffers or paid for the weekend beer. Happy days!

It would be wrong of me to leave that period without mentioning my digs in a very old, decrepit James I hunting lodge, which was falling apart around the owner's ears. It had become a small farm of some forty acres, run by 'T'owd Man','T'owd Lady', a middle-aged spinster daughter and a slightly younger, simple, brother. There were rooms for four lodgers and a common sitting/dining room and good food. Hot water, supplied from a 500-gallon tank, was available only on Friday nights, when all the household bathed in a huge bathroom, using a cast-iron bath, 7 foot long with a huge brass plug/overflow pipe, and so deep that I could only just see over the top. Everyone was limited to 45 minutes per bath! Otherwise a pan of warm water was provided for shaving in the morning, another to wash with at night.

'T'owd Lady', of indeterminate age, always wore a long, black shift to her ankles, slippers and a mob cap. The poor soul had a large growth on her cheek sprouting a hedgehog of black hairs and only ever said "Aye" or "Nay". When making the beds, which had feather mattresses, she collected the overlays, pulled them to the pillows and turned them down, so by Wednesday, everything only extended half-way down the bed which had to be re-made before retiring!

On my first night there, Peter Halsey, resident for some months, mentioned that the resident ghost was non-malevolent. I awoke at 1.30a.m. with wind howling outside to hear wheezing and groaning and a regular thump-thump on the stairs. Nearer to my room it came, while both door and window rattled violently. I must admit that I hid under the covers until the sounds faded away, then it took me ages to drop off again. Later, I discovered that it was 'T'owd Man' going to bed: he was both asthmatic and rheumatic! Then one morning I awoke as the bed-clothes were pulled over my head. I opened bleary eyes to the sight of 'T'owd Lady's' monstrous hairy hedgehog inches from my face. I reacted so violently that she uttered the only sentence I ever heard from her, "Ee! I'm sorry, I didna see ye there!"

Other tales belong to those days; finding the Priest Hole, where Tom slept, 'Drunken Duncan' falling out of my Austin 7 two-seater into the ditch on the way back from t'pub one January.

During the previous two years in Somerset, I had met and wooed a beautiful girl called Milly. I called her Gee, as she had green eyes. I fell hopelessly in love and we married in 1953, in March, in order to get the maximum tax rebate! Wonderful times, full of hard work, rugby, beer and laughter!

In January, 1953, the elements threw their full force against the East Coast. We were involved mostly with the Hull marshes, where I co-ordinated emergency plant and equipment. By March of that year, I had volunteered my services to Essex and was released from Yorkshire to take over the Dengie Pensinsula. I was installed with my bride in a one bedroom flat in Burnham on Crouch. We had packed all our worldly goods in my first new car, a Ford 8.

This was a marvellous time for a young engineer in charge of all he surveyed! Bob Tuck, the Clerk of Works, looked after seven Cost-Plus contracts. This meant that the contractors worked to my instruction and were paid 2½% on top of the total actual costs, under my control. We worked from 6 a.m. to 8 p.m., seven days a week - sometimes longer, based in the headquarters of the United States base for the Bradwell Air to Ground range, commanded by Captain Hank Reasonover, a typical, cigar-chewing, hard-swearing, generous American from the Windy City, Chicago, who could get hold of literally anything, including the typists! We ate, drank, slept well when the need arose, laughed a lot and worked bloody hard. In seven months we restored twenty-seven miles of damaged sea banks - then set about improving them.

I was to remain Resident Engineer, overseeing seven million pounds worth of sea bank improvement during the next two years, prior to my appointment as District Engineer for the Northern District of the Central Division of the Essex River Board, when I was able to play Rugby again and enjoy marital bliss. Many and varied were the jobs we tackled: major river work, large constructions all done by direct labour - we were proud of our expertise. Giving advice to major consultants and contractors, we had become experts in our field. One pleasure was the incredible collection of characters who worked with me; excavator drivers, gangers, under-foremen and so on, including Jack Thorogood.

From humble beginnings, Jack, at 17, joined the River Maintenance gang. In 1953, he was 47: an amiable giant of 6' 3" with a marshman's long, loping stride; a true countryman, the then foreman of the Dengie Hundred, liked and respected by everyone. In 1953, he successfully closed the major Dengie frontage breach with just 150 men, no mechanical plant and no meddlesome engineers - a rare feat, considering that the breach was a mile from the nearest hard road and had to be reached over flooded land. He was surely an iron man, a master of all facets of river and tidal bank work. he would lay the piece-work rate after working four hours at the operation himself, and was certainly the best scytheman I have ever seen, including the other Essex foremen.

He and his brother were renowned poachers, although never apprehended. He could call any bird or animal close enough to him to pick it up and could see things normal men would miss. Walking to the sea bank, he would take off his jacket and dive sideways, triumphantly arising with a kicking hare. He taught me all I know about wild-fowling and punt-gunning, full of stories of youthful escapades, but in company he was shy, and reticent about recalling the past. Living near an eminent pathologist he was often called, in the early hours, to help move 'stiffs', after which he and his partner would poach local pheasants, one holding the torch, Jack, (a dead shot at fifteen feet), using the catapult. The great man did not like shot in *his* pheasants! Jack laughed uproariously while recounting stories of his confederate's social visits to the land-owners and hearing their complaints about poaching.

In those days camaraderie abounded, with every man taking a pride in his job, but there was also plenty of fun.

One major construction job was extending a sluice outfall half a mile over the sand, which I had designed to be carried through the tide-cycle from 60 foot barges bolted together; my contacts with Marine Salvage were still extant and I hired everything from the Admiralty. A hole was dug under water and support piles driven. Each 60 foot long pipe of 4 foot diameter was floated into position, and as the tide ebbed, the hole was pumped and the pipe settled onto the piled bearers. The first pipe was lifted over the sea bank onto a timber ramp, to roll into the sea under the guidance, on site, of a young trainee engineer and four construction workers, also six extra men to assist in the operation. When I arrived on site, the pipe was stuck at the end of the ramp on a short projecting pile, hardly noticeable to the casual eye, but enough to stop the pipe's progress. My young engineer and the four construction workers were down to their underpants in four feet of water trying to lever off this pipe. The extra six men were idly watching. I blew my top, ordered them to help - they refused because they could not swim! Sacking them immediately, I joined the others and we accomplished the task. Then, instead of getting the motor boat, we walked and swam the pipe to the site easily. Fortunately, it was a beautiful June day.

Engineers came from all over to watch proceedings, and the Chief Engineer decided to bring the whole Board to view the works. On the day, the timing of the tide was right and everyone arrived on the sea bank as we started pumping out the hole. The young engineer's task was to stand on the pipe, (which had four steadying lines to prevent rolling), and make certain it settled on the bearers. He was the key player, and strolled nonchalantly to and fro, even stopping to roll a cigarette. Then the pipe imperceptibly began to roll; the foreman held the steadying lines in his hand and grinning, indicated, "watch this!" The water went down and the pipe continued to roll, slowly at first, then faster. Realisation of his predicament dawned on the young man. He managed to keep upright, and to the cheers of the Board members, leapt desperately for solid land. He missed! Every time he tried to climb out, the bank collapsed to more cheers. Finally, we took pity and threw him a line. He struggled over the sea bank and in a muddy, bedraggled state, plodded back to the site hut, the assembled crowd applauding. As his shirt, etc. would dry in the sun I offered him my trousers to save him going home. There was work to be done. The young man in question, James Robertson, went on to become a partner in an eminent firm of consulting engineers.

For me, in due course, promotion followed, and by 1960, I had attained the elevated title of Deputy Area Engineer to the newly re-organised Southern Area. About this time, I started a consultancy, designing under-drainage schemes, farm irrigation and reservoirs; a business which took off resulting in my working eighteen hours a day - back to working hard and playing hard!

The moonlighting was the cause of a falling out with the Ministry Regional Engineer, a man who demanded 'T's' crossed and 'I's' dotted - unlike my clients who had no time for all that nonsense. Eventually he wrote to our Chief Engineer, listing all the ad hoc works carried out and asking if he was aware of my activities. The first outcome of this was an invitation to lunch with our chairman and congratulations on my resourcefulness, coupled with a letter to the Ministry Engineer informing him that the Board backed the useful services provided their ratepayers. The second result was, however, a directive that any other staff member must gain the Board's approval before engaging in similar activities.

My feeling was that I had reached a cross-road. Should I go independent or remain employed? A hard choice when we had two kids and a mortgage. The decision was taken for me. A peptic ulcer was diagnosed and the consultancy had to be cut down whilst I retained the security of employment. By coincidence, an offer to contract came my way, which perhaps I should have accepted. I was also still into rugby, progressing into representative fields, but although sitting on the bench twice for Eastern Counties, a Cap was to elude my grasp. However, my first love blossomed: I became an ardent keel-boat sailor - of other people's: we were too impecunious, or maybe found it too easy to spend most of what was earned!

At this period, the Area Engineer left for pastures new and I thought my hard work over the years should hold me in good stead, but the magic of 'letters' after a name meant the post went to a charming man, a good rugby player, albeit of ex-Head Office design, firmly believing in toeing the Head Office line, discouraging non-conformist initiative. It was time to move on, and where better for a Drainage Engineer than the Fens? It was a great wrench to leave the people with whom I had worked, laughed and played rugby, but the family were growing up and we needed money.

In 1966, on joining the Welland and Nene River Authority as Divisional Engineer based in Stamford, I was to discover that we, the staff, consisted of just two - a young engineer and me! But once again I found more wonderful characters to work with.

To carry out the major improvement of the River Welland we built up a direct labour construction organisation. This operation was to culminate in the Flood Alleviation Scheme for Market Harborough which was carried out almost entirely from staging in the river, as factories lined both banks. The river went through the industrial centre of the town.

The construction was controlled by our General Construction Foreman, Garry Saunders. Garry and I rarely saw eye to eye, but after several pints of ale, we compromised on a workable solution, the "design boys" predicted that our construction methods would not work, they did! *And* we cut the estimate by forty percent and gained a reputation for achieving the ultimate without interference from senior management!

My young engineer had now moved on and his replacement was Malcolm Howell, an extremely capable and ultra-hardworking chap. He was of genuine land drainage stock, nothing being too much trouble, no hours too long; happy to work at any time or day and, like me, a lover of good ale. We enjoyed a number of years of supreme comradeship, working together to the highest order, not least in the 'Saga of Ryhall'!

This episode began with the planning authorities allowing a housing estate to be built in the flood plain. Naturally, it was liable to flood. In 1968, a severe storm passed over the Fens, the rainfall so heavy that the upper reaches of the River Gwash overtopped its banks; a flood was imminent at Ryall. Estimating that the peak would occur at two o'clock in the morning, by six the previous evening Malcolm and I were stationed at the top end, (high ground), of the village in my Dormobile.

Having assessed the rate of rise of the river, we advised the Police to warn the residents of the estate to either evacuate their properties or move upstairs. We discovered that the old village pub was also at risk and helped the landlord to lift carpets, seats and movables onto suitable tables - with appropriate recompense, of course!

By 11p.m. the flood water had reached the estate and the pub's regulars set off home before their feet got wet. By midnight, there were already 6 inches of water in the pub; the landlord, accompanied by a lifelong chum, despite the water running up the exhaust pipe of his new Jaguar, parked outside, remained cheerful, whilst most of the residents of the estate had moved their furniture and carpets upstairs and were waiting for the peak.

At midnight, we warned the landlord that he was likely to be flooded to a depth of 3 feet. 'Oh, Christ! My pigs!" he cried.

Splashing down to the pigsty, we found sixteen piglets swimming round with mum, her arse just above the water-line. What followed is firmly imprinted on my mind: wriggling piglets caught, passed hand-to-hand, until finally deposited in the Buffalos' Hall above the stables, water nearly to the top of our thigh-boots, pulling and pushing the sow up the steps; the landlord and his chum, soaked and covered all over in "Sweet Violets", our protective clothing filthy, the water by now over 3 feet in the bar; the top coming off a fresh bottle of Scotch; we left the two of them, laughing helplessly, sitting on a settee perched on a table, wrapped in blankets and nothing else. At 2.20 a.m., the water now subsiding, Malcolm and I returned to the Dormobile to sleep.

At 7.30 in the morning, the landlord woke us with a full cooked breakfast on a tray, coffee, toast, a bottle of Scotch and two glasses. The reward of a Land Drainage Engineer!

Over the years, I have assisted in the rescue from floods of every kind of animal, which meant getting very wet. We have saved a prize bull, thoroughbred horses, (both very frightened and difficult to handle), and even a stag whose antlers were caught in the bushes.

In 1970, we were all set to combine three Upland Divisions and embark on a crash programme of improvement to rivers, sluices, bridges, weirs and syphons, also miles of tree clearance and excavation. The major structures were built by Garry Saunders and three other construction gangs organised by a new side-kick, Dennis Fenn, a fiery, argumentative, hard-working miracle-maker. Once again we reached compromises over the inevitable jug of ale! These were heady days for everyone involved in the works' office, with young men being thrust in at the deep end when it came to responsibility and decision making. It was very much a case of 'If you don't like the heat, get out of the kitchen' and surprisingly enough very few clangers were dropped.

During this period, my wife and I built a new house overlooking the River Nene, incorporating old stone from mills and bridges. There are eight types of stone in the chimney breast, the lintel being the Date Stone of the original Market Harborough Bridge. This was our dream home where we settled down, prepared to end our days in our nest. It was not to be. Instructed to now combine the two Fen Divisions back to Flatlands. I faced another challenge, but not one appreciated by the family as we had to leave our house and move to Wisbech.

The Flatlands, which were under the influence of Tidal Protection, were my first love, the wheel had turned full circle. We handled stones for training works on the Welland and Nene with our own barges and tugs, even had our own sea-going launch. There was, of course, the usual collection of characters. One was a new assistant, Geoff Beal, yet another opinionated, conscientious extrovert, who followed the tradition of working long hours without complaint and with whom we created a great team of hard-working land drainage artisans. Why does working with tides mould such fine attitudes, such as the work hard, play hard philosophy, I wonder?

Having started work on the main river element of the North Level, we were proceeding at a great pace, when there came the advent of the Anglian Water Authority, which, in my opinion, was detrimental because land drainage became very small fry.

It was a great relief to me to be approached by the great Dick Berry and asked whether I would be interested in undertaking the Engineer's position in the North Level Internal Drainage Board in 1975. Having known Dick for some years, when he was the chairman of the Welland and Nene River Authority Works Committee, I looked forward to working with him. I was to be the Engineer in Charge of the North Level Improvement Scheme, an incredible opportunity for an engineer. After a lifetime of river and drainage engineering, I am sincerely grateful to Dick Berry and his Board for entrusting me with their confidence.

I have always treasured the comradeship and effort that went into taming nature whilst furthering the Herculean endeavours of our forebears who created the fertile flatlands of Britain. Their single-mindedness, perseverance and foresight never ceases to amaze me.

Land drainage, river engineering and sea defence work is the only branch of civil engineering which provides a practical engineer with the ultimate satisfaction, mainly because of its closeness to nature and the elements, also because knowledge of the behaviour of these elements is an inexact science, which can only be acquired by experience.

Event prediction by computer can only be a tool of the experienced, and should never be taken as fact.

After a lifetime in land drainage I can only be absolutely certain of two things:

One: there will always be a flood greater than the last big one.

Two: variations in nature, climate, rainfall and tidal changes are cyclic.

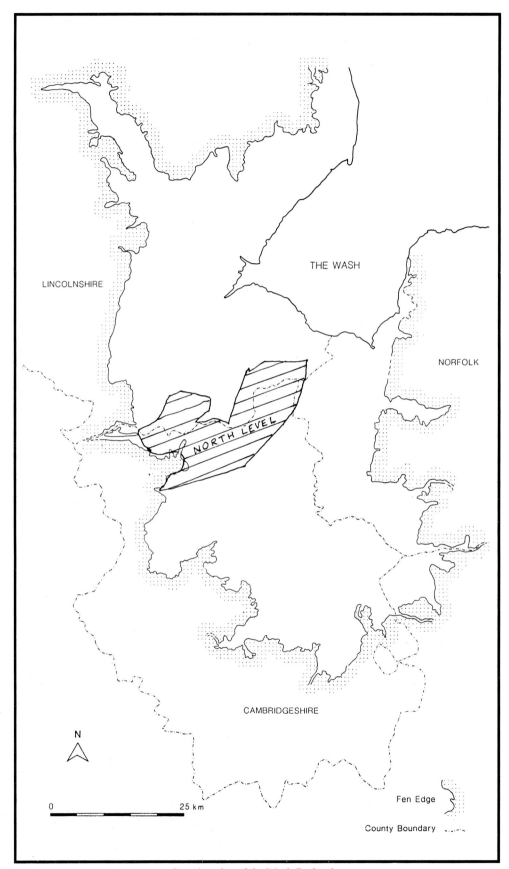

Location plan of the Wash Fenlands

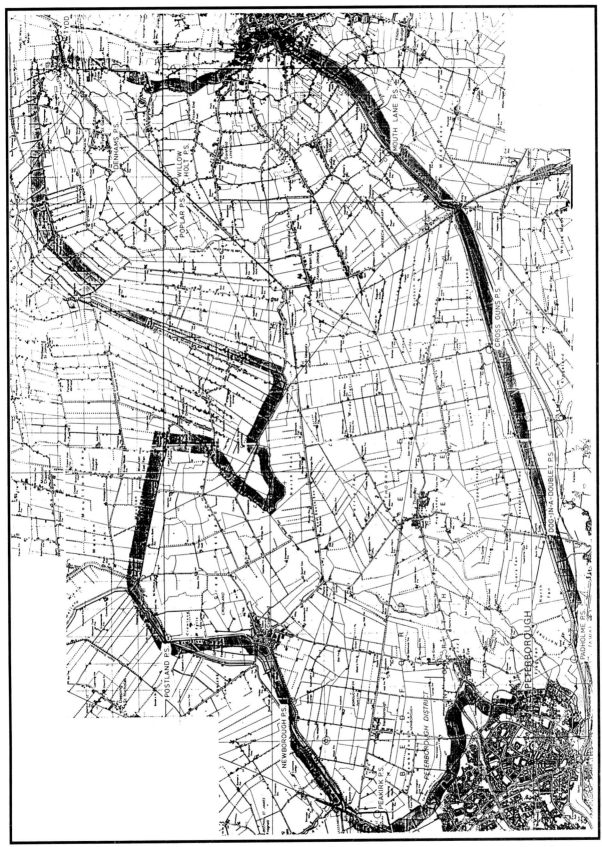

The North Level Area

CHAPTER II

The Geological Formation of the North Level

The geographical area in this book covers the present area of the North Level Internal Drainage Board. This part of the Fens is bounded in the south by the River Nene and in the north by the River Welland to Four Mile Bar. It extends from Peterborough in the west to Tydd Gote/Foul Anchor to the east. The present Fens, covering several hundred square miles, stretch from Lincoln to Cambridge inland from Peterborough to Huntingdon and surround the Wash. The area comprises two different types of ground, the Marsh and the Fen. The Marsh extends fifteen miles inland from the present coastline and consists of wholly marine deposits of silt, clay and some peat. The Fen is mainly between the Marsh and the Uplands and consists of Blacklands comprising peat and humus-rich black soil. The Rivers Witham, Glen, Welland, Nene, Great Ouse, Little Ouse, Lark and Nar all discharge through the Flatlands to the Wash. This vast catchment has contributed almost as much to the complicated sedimentation of the Fen basin as the incursions of the sea.

Many eminent geologists, archaeologists and botanists have been fascinated by the strata of deposits laid down in the Fens, and have perfected ways of dating soils through pollens. In recent years, carbon dating has recorded their findings. These experts have provided a reasonably accurate picture of the inhabitants of the Fens and their way of life, in particular the development of the domestication of animals and arable farming, which is interesting to the Land Drainage Engineers, as successful arable cultivation cannot be achieved without drainage.

When the last Ice Age ended about 7500 BC, the rivers cut their way through the clays into the North Sea and growth was established along the river banks, with an estimated temperature rise, 3^0 C greater than today's average annual temperature, conditions in the Fens were ideal for rapid colonisation by birch and pine, then deciduous trees, elm, oak and ash, covering the area with a dense forest apart from the river flood plains and glacial holes.

Around 5500 BC, the climate became wetter and colder; the overspill from the rivers became more prevalent; probably because the rising sea levels restricted out-flow. On wetter ground the deciduous trees died whilst the Alder, the drainage Engineers' friend as its horizontal tap roots along river banks prevent soil erosion, spread in the river washlands. Although cooler, it was warmer than today, with higher average ambient temperatures and the Fenland forest was at its peak; full of animals long since extinct, and a paradise for the hunter. But the sea level was rising rapidly and the glacial clays in the North Sea eroding, until finally the sea invaded the Fenland forests. About 3000 BC, the Fen hunters ceased to be nomadic and became part time farmers in forest clearings, along with hunting and fishing.

The varying thickness of the Fen clay deposited can be explained by the engineering characteristics of Tidal Channel flow. The vast reservoir of salt water in the North Sea, laden with sand, silt and clay particles in suspension flows up the rivers and tidal creeks. As the level rises, in order to flow, there must be a gradient to the surface. This is achieved by the level rising higher at the outfall, in order to overcome the resistance to flow caused by the friction of the channel banks and beds; this required rise slows down the tidal flow and the larger particles of sand are deposited; first the silt and then the clay. When the water reaches a level where it spills out, vegetation adjacent to the channel collects the clay and this continues as the water progresses across the Flatland until finally it runs out of suspended matter. Therefore, there is a far greater depth of sand and silt adjacent to the sea than some distance inland. As the tide rises, deposits accelerate in the Flatland as rivers and creeks silt up, but more gradually. About one quarter inch of consolidated silt remains on the banks after 100 tides. Where there is vegetation, up to an eighth of an inch of silt can be deposited per tide. These are present day figures, but in 2000 BC the particle load of the tide was far greater due to the erosion of the bed of the North Sea.

The rise in the ground level adjacent to creeks and rivers prevented the natural drainage of the Flatland and vast areas of rotting growth, now covered in clay and silt, became flooded shallowly with brackish stagnant water. The peat now formed under the clay became the first Fenland peat layer. At this time also, the upland rivers were still cutting their way through the valley floors, becoming laden with gravel, sand and clay particles. River channels obey the same channel flow laws as tidal creeks, but the head required is supplied by the steep bed gradients in the upland. When the bed gradient changes from steep to flat, the velocity drops and deposition of suspended particles commences. If the flow is too great for the Flatland channel, banks will overtop and finer particles are deposited. This accelerates as the channels, at the change of gradient, become clogged with sand and gravel. The fresh water mixed with the salt water, produces a brackish environment still evident in Marshland drains today. This continuation of fresh water inundation finally produced conditions suitable for re-establishment of growth. In the early part of the second millenium BC, the tidal rise had slowed and the deposits on the banks of creeks and bed rises permitted only the highest tides to reach inland areas. The second peat layer began building up.

A period of warmer weather ensued, encouraging growth which finally raised levels of the land making natural drainage possible to the rivers and creeks. Once this happened, the rate of growth and specie flora accclerated.

The second Fenland peat layer was adjacent to the River Nene in the south and the River Welland in the north except for odd pockets of open water to the east, which finally became peat. The experts tell us that there was a further incursion of the sea around 500 AD which extended the silt deposit areas inland, eventually filling up the creeks and raising the bed of the rivers where they entered the sea.

However, I interpret the silt deposits differently, unconvinced that this was a sudden incursion; although there was an acceleration of tidal rise during the second temperate era, an infiltration of silt into the Flatlands was over a long period. Growth on the tidal banks was sparse, therefore the rise of the bank could not keep abreast of the tide rise, allowing a greater area to be flooded with silt and clay-laden water. As I previously demonstrated, each tide carried a considerably quantity of clay and silt particles and each spring tide now had access to a wider area. I believe my theory is borne out by the fact that in the clay and silt areas of the North Level, the second peat layer is very thin - not more than four inches thick.

About AD 500, this silt incursion had filled in all the tidal creeks, known today as Roddons, and raised the beds of the river outfalls so much that channels were unable to take the upland floods regularly inundating vast areas of inland Fenland, producing inland lakes like Whittlesey, Mere and Knarr Lake, Newborough Lake and a small one near Newton in the North Level area.

There is evidence of Roman farming near the Catswater, Old South Eau and Shire Drain on the higher ground close to this main artery, possibly the northern arm of the River Nene which met the Welland at Crowland. Although it has not been investigated, my knowledge of the ground levels indicates this channel was maintained and improved by the Romans to give water access from their settlements to the Car Dyke in Peterborough; confirmed perhaps, by the fact that this channel cuts through the first Glacial Age gravel deposits at Powder Blue to the east of Newborough Fen. The silt deposits overlying the Roman agricultural settlements signal the failure of the Roman embanking to contain spring tides and tidal surges, doubtless hastened by lack of maintenance, or malicious damage inflicted by Saxon invaders after AD 450: the Anglo-Romans being defeated by the Saxons in AD 577.

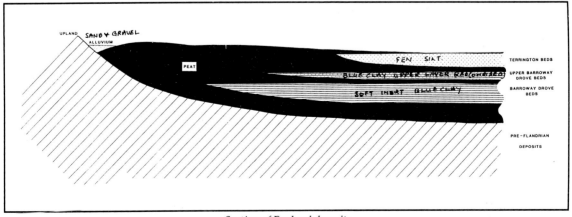

Section of Fenland deposits

CHAPTER III

The Early Farmer Drainers, AD 43 - AD 1066

Evidence exists of Anglo-Roman occupation of the silt lands adjacent to the Shire Drain, alongside the ancient branch of the River Nene, to Throckenholt and beyond, and along the high ground of the Catswater. The Romans realised their arable cereal crops needed keeping dry; aerial evidence shows outlines of settlements with fields surrounded by ditches and homesteads on higher ground, successfully growing woad, wheat and barley. After Boadicea's defeat, many Britons were probably deported to the Fens as slaves to develop the Roman Fenland Estate in the maritime silt and clay land and Fen edges. The only way of transporting produce was by water. The Romans cut the canal from Cambridge to Lincoln connecting their major garrisons, they also improved the ancient channel from Peterborough to the sea at Tydd, giving access to the settlement of the Northern Fenland Estate.

During the Roman era, 45 BC to AD 400, because of increased tide rises, danger of inundation and silt deposit, embankments were raised in the marsh around Tydd and Wisbech, thus producing ditch drainage and short distance foot and cattle movement on the bank during flooding.

Halfway through the Roman era, the Saxons were invading remote Fenland areas, often sacking homesteads and breaking down banks. At the end of the Roman occupation, AD 436, much previously cultivated land was covered in a layer of maritime silt. Uncultivated wet clayland carried a meagre growth of sedge and other freshwater plants, ultimately submerged in maritime silt. The area became sparsely populated until the Saxons defeated the Anglo-Romans, in AD 577, and realised the potential of the old and new silt lands.

The Saxons brought with them long-standing techniques of crop husbandry, including the ability to break up heavy land and consolidated silt with oxen team ploughs. At this time, Christianity took hold and the warring early Saxon kings changed the sword for the plough. Little is known of the Anglo-Saxons' drainage works except perhaps that many channels to the sea in the North Level were kept open, despite silting, and the Roman banks were restored. During the late seventh century, minor embankments were constructed reclaiming small areas as far west as Crowland and north-west of Wisbech.

The Saxons discovered that the fertility of the silt land only lasted a few years with continual cropping, then reverted to rough grass. This encouraged the settlers to create new embanked areas for arable land and to keep sheep as an aid to fertility. The only cattle were oxen, required for tillage, which had to be watered from collected rain as that in the drains and ponds was saline. These developments were the first step towards crop rotation in the Fens.

The monasteries at Peterborough, in AD 665, Thorney, in AD 662, and Crowland, in 712 AD, (all initially refuges for religious hermits), created an awareness of the agricultural potential and benefits of land ownership. The Hundreds of Wisbech is recorded to have had 70,790 acres of cultivated land, from Sutton St Edmund in the west to Marshland in the south. The monasteries did major work to improve and extend their holdings, building the great Welland Bank to Crowland and Brotherhouse Bar, and raising the Car Dyke banks. Water transport channels were cut both north and south of Thorney linking up with Peterborough.

For two centuries, the monasteries reclaimed more by embanking. The monks were excellent farmers, utilising crop rotation and maintaining large herds of cattle and sheep. They also became exceedingly wealthy and greedy; claiming ownership of the undrained marsh land, requiring tithes from inhabitants, resulting in land boundary disputes between Thorney, Crowland, Peterborough and Ely. All agricultural progress, however, was destroyed by Scandinavian invaders in the days of pillage and rape's which continued until the Restoration of the Monasteries between AD 970 and AD 980.

Previous researchers noted successful reclamation of the land by increasing numbers of cattle and sheep, and that cereal crops grew around Crowland and Thorney on the higher clay and silt lands. However, much of the North Level was covered in shallow, stagnant, brackish water with occasional deeper meres: uninhabitable, dank and vaporous from methane gas, producing rotting vegetation, a breeding ground for the malaria carrying Anophalous Mosquito. Most settlers and monks living on higher ground escaped the scourge, but inhabitants on the Fen edges suffered greatly from the Ague, (Malaria), with its horrific hallucinatory effect. Obviously Fenland accounts of hobgoblins, devils and other frightening manifestations date from this. Read St. Guthlac's account of his trials, 'Dugdale on the Fens' 1772. Malaria was not stamped out in the area until 1927.

Reclamation of land, able to grow hay in the summer, but unusable in the winter, due to flooding, lasted only another hundred years. The Scandinavians, wintering in the Fen areas and attacking settlements, arrived in force in AD 780. The prosperous areas of the North Level, around Wisbech, along the South Eau, Thorney, Peterborough and Crowland were pillaged and looted, the monasteries sacked in AD 870, flood defences broken down, and the last English king, St. Edmund, killed.

The Scandinavians had settled in the North of England earlier and gradually moved south into Lincolnshire. King Alfred, after some resistance, agreed to settlement. Little evidence remains of settlement in the North Level, some in the Tydd area, but most lying to the north-east of Peterborough and Deeping. A hundred years of turbulence followed, with incursions by other Scandinavians, until some stability was achieved by Canute in AD 1016, who divided the country into four Earldoms. Edgar, his successor, restored the monasteries together with their previous drainage and embanking works, but many of the settlements had been destroyed although the original Saxon settlements in Tydd, Newton and Leverington survived.

Peace came finally when Canute was made King in 1017.

In the Tydd area and along the Old South Eau, evidence remains of the old Saxon Field, Drove and Drain systems. One can envisage the landscape in AD 1000 and earlier, from vantage points on the Shire Drain, the Old South Eau, and at Thorney. Knowing the location of Black Fen Edge, the area covered by the Black Fen Morass, which was some 6 to 8 feet above the present level, is traceable. Much of David Hall's work, establishing old deposits in the Level, resulted from the close liaison with the North Level, particularly where channels were cut during the recent major scheme there. Ordnance levels of exposed strata and spot levels on detailed maps of the region were supplied. All this investigation in the office, looking at old maps, identifying strata in the field, was to give us an intimate knowledge of the area and a lasting interest in its history.

Before joining the North Level, I was the Engineer for the Fens with the Water Authority, and together we assisted Francis Prior, the County Archaeologist, and his group, at the start of the Flag Fen Village dig. Happy hours were spent in the winter at the Dog and Doublet Pub, studying old maps and sections. I showed Francis some old piles pulled out of the Padholme Drain during widening, which he recognised as pre-Roman. We exposed a section of the old Roman causeway, with a more ancient track beneath, the start of a major archeological find, the only one of its type in the country.

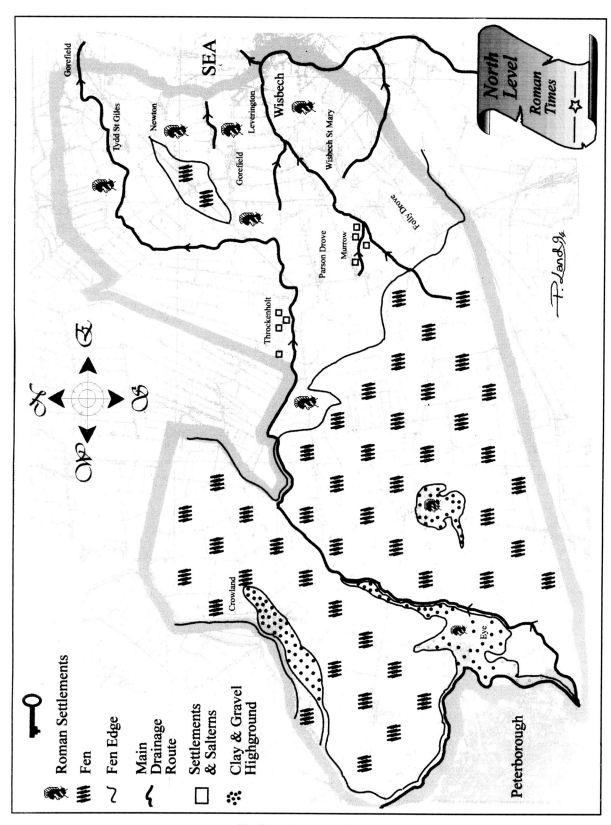

North Level in Roman Times

CHAPTER IV

The Time of the Awakening: AD 1066 - 1600

The Norman invasion was sudden and spectacularly successful. William of Normandy, (William I), was made King in 1066. The Domesday Inquest of AD 1087. showed the North Level area populated with only five people and less than two oxen teams per thousand acres. Compared to the western part of the Level, the northern part of the Hundreds of Wisbech, Tydd and Newton were highly prosperous. The Hundred was an administrative region between the village and the Shire, dating back to the early 9th Century, supposedly an area of one hundred hides; a hide being territory which would support one peasant family. The administrative unit consisted of a body of freeholders, presided over by a Hundreds Reeve, the representative of the Crown. They dealt with petty criminals, boundary disputes and, until 1285, drainage matters. After this time the Courts of Sewers were set up specifically for drainage, but covered the same area as the Hundred.

The administrative Hundreds were to be superseded by District Councils created by the Local Government Act of 1894.

In the predominantly Danish Counties, the Hundreds were called Wapantakes, in Suffolk, Norfolk and Essex, Leets, in Kent, Lathes, and in the North West, Wards.

The settlements at Crowland and Thorney were obviously too small to be mentioned - perhaps the monasterial edict forbidding women to reside within six miles of the monastery, thus ensuring celibacy by preventing temptation, had something to do with it. Maybe this was the origin of the Fen tale that Fenmen got their women from the Uplands, then died of the ague in two years. This reduction of population in some 200 hundred years must have resulted from the Scandinavians pillaging and raping, leading to neglect of flood defences so there was little left to pillage, few rape victims.

The tide was still rising and the estuary of the Great Wisbech River continued to silt up. As already mentioned, the relatively sudden rise of the tide causing inundation and silt, clogging the outfalls, occurred 500-600 years earlier. Accretion in the Wash has continued ever since and is analogous to a sudden local enlargement of a river which causes the velocity to drop, producing eddies where the flow cannot carry the silt load and drops it. The North Sea is a kind of vast tidal river flowing north to south and reverse, meeting the enlargement of the Wash and giving rise to silt deposit.

The embankments were raised to contain the tide, but could not hold the local rise in water levels on spring tides accompanied by north to north-easterly gales. Gales can increase the coastal water four feet or more by blowing in the surface of the water, and there is danger of fresh-water-flooding on the rivers. Successive embankments constructed along the river to prevent summer flooding restricted the spread of water and raised the winter flood level in the river. Settlers in the 11th century were not aware that the river channel needed widening, and erected embankments to prevent water levels rising, so as the banks were raised and land reclaimed, encouraging husbandry, failure of banks caused breaches and immediate flooding. As the problems worsened, a need for community efforts developed to counteract them, especially regarding the maintenance and improvement of the embankments along the major drainage channels.

The Roman Bank through Leverington and Newton to four Gotes is part of the major mediaeval bank construction surrounding the Wash. This most likely resulted from the Petition to the Crown by the people of Leverington, Newton, Fitton, Tydd and Wisbech - and even as far away as Gorefield - following the disastrous floods of 1246 AD. This was a major construction, being some 15 feet high with a 6 foot top width, and earth ramparts at 200 to 300 yard intervals. These ramparts, about 300 yards long with a top width of 50 feet, pointed in a south-easterly direction to divert north-easterly waves - the vulnerable direction to the Wash - away from the main embankments. This embankment extended from Four Gotes to Horseshoe Corner at Wisbech, then across the east side of the estuary. The river banks to Guyhirn were also raised, together with the old South Eau, (Murrow), banks to Cloughs Cross. In 1616 A.D. it was stated that this bank was 'for defending of lands in the Level from the Force and Rage of the Sea'.

Tidal rises in the thirteenth and fourteenth centuries resulted from an overall rise in the earth's temperature - a mediaeval 'Global Warming' - and the subsequent melting of the ice-caps, there are historical references to vineyards around Wisbech. This embankment would have protected a far greater area than mentioned, stretching inland as far as Peterborough, and was a major civil engineering construction, which prevented inundations of thousands of acres in the North Level. Ancient customs and rights of drainage carried with them responsibilities.

In AD 1087, William 11, (Rufus), succeeded his father. After his death in AD 1100, his younger brother, Henry 1, claimed the throne; his other brother, Duke Henry, being away on crusades. Henry 1 immediately married Eadgyth, (Edith), daughter of the Scots King and great granddaughter of Edmund Ironside, forming a neat alliance of the Scottish and English Crowns thereby, avoiding trouble from the north. He concentrated on defeating his brother's invasion to claim the crown and also rid himself of many troublesome Norman noblemen. He ruled the country peacefully and humanely for thirty years. The influence of the abbots and priors had increased since restoration of the monasteries by Edgar between AD 970 and 980; by the time Henry I came to the Throne, in AD 1100, their power and wealth rivalled that of the Barons, who had little interest in the dark, dank Fens.

According to ancient drainage custom, whoever reclaimed the land by embanking was required to maintain the banks. However, the tithes and rents the abbots extracted from tenants of reclaimed land filled their own coffers, while their tenants maintained the banks fronting their land, a convenient arrangement for the abbots. Much of the reclamation was around Crowland and the higher land north of Thorney, with further extensions on siltland at Tydd, Leverington and Newton. The Black Fen regions in the level had become Meres and Pools which, as common land, were fished by farmers and others who got their living from these 'vaporous areas' in the winter. In AD 1086, the annual render to the Abbot of Ely was 33,260 sticks of eels, (a stick held 25 eels and was the method of their transportation). During the next hundred years, Fenmen strove to extend their arable holdings by embanking; much of the previous arable area was now down to grass and the banks were maintained under the ancient Assart Rights and Customs which, with more embanked areas, were often ignored or responsibility for their upkeep refuted by landlords. Conditions did not improve until King John signed the Magna Carta and Henry II succeeded him. In every century, landlords are loth to spend without an immediate return for their money.

Henry II became King in 1153. He and his ministers laid down the Laws and Customs of Drainage in Romney Marsh in AD 1222, which became the basis of deciding individual responsibility to the community for sewers and embankments; Henry passed the first Land Drainage Act in 1258, setting up the Court of Sewers which adjudicated on the responsibilities of barons, abbots and their tenants, with travelling judges to hear presentments at each Court. 'Sewer', was at that time the official term for a natural or man-made channel, whilst 'clows' was the term for sluices.

Knowing what ought to be done to maintain and improve the system, was a different matter from carrying out the tasks. Many and varied were protests to the Court about neighbours' works - or lack of them, improvements to be paid for by the barons and abbots were usually passed on to their tenants, and Commissioners of Sewers for each 'Hundred' were appointed to ensure that the Courts' decisions were implemented. They also had responsibility for preventing damage to banks by cattle, etc. In this connectio, is recorded that, in 1190 AD, Wisbech Barton was exempted from paying taxes in fairs and markets in order to finance the repair of the banks of the Great Wisbech River.

In 1236, a tidal flood inundated the North Level, causing considerable damage and loss of life, with thousands of animals being drowned. Tenants of Wisbech, Leverington, Tydd and Newton presented a Petition of Evidence of the siltation of the outfall of the Great Wisbech River, which resulted in the King ordering all the banks to be heightened and strengthened. money was raised by the tenants and people of Wisbech: nothing was done to the outfall.

At this time, the South Eau branched at Cloughs Cross; one arm going northwards along Lady Nunn Eau and Shire Drain, the other into the Great Wisbech River at Guyhirn: a great bank on the east side protecting the north side of the Hundred of Wisbech Court of Sewers area.

The whole of the North Level, except for Sutton St Edmund Common, drained into the River Nene or the estuary at Guyhirn, Wisbech, Four Gotes and Tydd. Sutton St Edmund Common discharged northwards via Fleet to the sea, but was initially drowned and unproductive. The Porsand area, north-west of Crowland, was also virtually drowned, but discharged into the South Eau via Dowesdale.

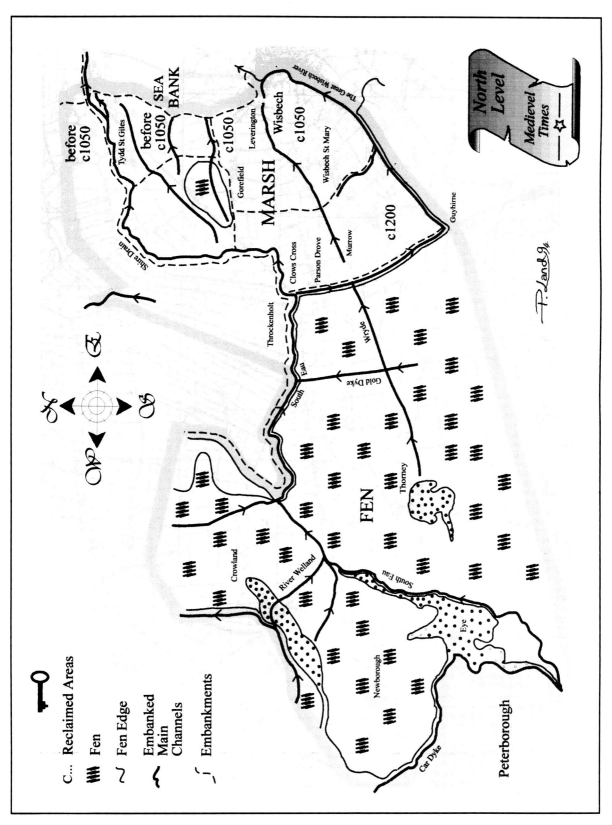

North Level in Medieval Times

The Medieval Sea Bank

Dugdale, in his 'Treatise of Drainage and Imbanking' noted that: "Irruption of the Sea caused by N & NE winds on a high tide were casual and these floods did not remain on the land to destroy by drowning, the stagnation of fresh water flooded produced much more damage...". Records of the Commissioners of Sewers show that maintenance of embankments was of paramount importance, especially around Wisbech in the Hundred.

In 1260, fresh water from the uplands, combining with high tides, overtopped embankments and inundated some 35,000 acres, causing great losses. This catastrophe occured frequently during the next centuries, flooding a similar acreage each time as deteriorating banks were breached. As late as 1947 a similar area was flooded.

In 1274, there was a disaster from which the North Level was unable to recover until the new outfall channel to the River Nene was cut in the nineteenth century. At this time the Little and Great Ouse discharged into the River Nene at Wisbech. This combined fresh water flow helped to keep the outfall clear of silt, or rather reduced the acceleration of silting of the estuary which was then apparent.

During 1274, the people of Littleport cleaned out an old Roman canal and that winter, a major flood broke the bank of the Little Ouse which flowed down the canal into the River Lark, thence to King's Lynn to become the new course of the Little Ouse. In one foul winter's night the destiny of the Nene outfall and the North Level changed, with the considerably reduced flow of the River Nene unable to keep the siltation of outfall at bay. In 1275, Hugh de Balsham assigned to the Monks of Ely, who claimed this flooded land, the task of embanking and reclaiming Wisbech High Fen, land west of the outfall of the South Eau at Guyhirn, but their efforts failed, the area remained tide swept and inundated with fresh water floods.

From then, the occupants of the North Level marsh around Wisbech fought a continual battle to hold back the sea and maintain drainage to a rapidly silting outfall; it was not known that drainage of marshland results in land shrinkage. Things became so disastrous that in 1301 a dam was constructed in Well Creek to direct the Ouse flow back to Wisbech. This produced a major saga of land drainage legislation lasting 30 years, until, in 1438, the successors of the dam erectors were instructed by the King to remove it under Pain of Death. Dugdale's account insight into the difficulties the officers of the Court of Sewers experienced in dealing with communal responsibilities of this nature, due to lack of legal authority. However, nothing was done about the Little Ouse and the Nene and the outfall continued to deteriorate.

In 1290, the Commissioner had instructed tenants in Tydd, Newton and Leverington to repair banks to prevent fresh water issuing into the Fen. Adam de Tydd agreed to this, providing the high lands along Shire Drain was not 'charged', (not affected by floods). Further orders followed, and in 1297, Geoffrey de Sandiacre was commanded to view the banks and issue repair orders. After presentments, in AD 1314, Edward II instructed Geoffrey de Colville to examine the banks at Newton and Wish St Mary 'then in decay...', and repair them. This instruction was repeated 21 years later in AD 1335, after major flooding. There was a 25 year gap from 1953-1978 between serious indundations, watch out for 2003!

The thirteenth and fourteenth centuries showed continued reclamation activity in the small silt and clay areas north of Thorney toward Crowland, south-east of Crowland in Newborough, north and south of Gorefield; small embankments, enclosing areas with their own 'GOAT" to prevent freshwater flooding. These were known as Private Banks, whereas the main Sewers, (channels with banks either side), were 'Banks under the control of the Dyke Reeves and Commissioners of Sewers'. The upkeep of these minor banks led to the tenants refuting their responsibility for main sewer banks unless these affected them directly: resulting in more orders being issued by the Court of Sewers. William Clapton, Abbot of Thorney, built a house in the midst of Thorney Fen, surrounded by ditches. Progress was being made!

A petition in AD 1395, held at Fleet, maintained that'[the] portion of land in Sutton and Tydd is so low that....they are yearly drowned....'. This led to the Lady Nunn Eau being replaced by a new straight channel now known as Straightreach. Presentments were made in AD 1395, to make up the Welland Bank, Southeau Bank and Dowesdale Bank; work was carried out immediately, as these banks were owned by the Crown and protected Crown Land.

The numerous petitions to the Commissioners of Sewers show the ever-increasing problems of private embanking affecting areas not embanked; the fresh water flood had to spill out somewhere, preferably the lowest ground.

In AD 1438, Henry VI ordered St John Colville to repair Wisbech Fendyke, cleanse the South Eau to Throckenholt, and the Bishop of Thorney via Cloughs Cross to Guyhirn. This was after excess flooding in Northside, by the major beaches in Fen Dyke, or Murrow Bank, still there today. There were other drainage Acts in the fifteenth Century, which only extended the term of office of Commissioners who were given no teeth to enforce action. More difficulties arose because some Commissioners were also landowners who put their own interests first!!

The first significant Land Drainage Engineering works in the North Level were carried out by Bishop Morton of Peterborough who cut a new straight channel from Stanground to Guyhirn and straightened the Great Wisbech River to Rummers Mill (P.S.). The major part of the River Nene flow was directed down this straight channel and the importance of the North and South arms declined. This marginally reduced the danger of bank failure along the South Eau and Shire Drain and improved the Guyhirn outfall, but the outfall below Wisbech was still silting up.

The Land Drainage Act of 1531 finally recognised the need for statutory powers to resolve the conflicts of communal responsibility for banks and sewers. It became a felony to maliciously damage banks: a crime punishable by death - power indeed! The 'Acre-Shot Levy' was introduced for the maintenance of banks and sewers, based on the owner's land holding, giving the Commissioners power to raise a Byelaw in times of great need, ie breaches. This acre-shot levy was raised on land which received benefit and protection from banks and sewers and created the basis for future legislation. Callis, in 1622, tried to trace and clarify the development of the Court of Sewers and explain the restraints in force.

The fourteenth and fifteenth centuries saw little effort made to reclaim areas of the Fen - all improvements were to the Marsh, including the first tidal reclamation in Tydd and along the Wisbech estuary in 1490. This was probably because the Fen was useful for turf, (Turbary), mowing, sedge, reeds and rushes for thatching, hazel and buckthorn for wattle fencing, sheep pens, etc., together with fish and wildfowl. The land was also valuable for grazing in the summer, designated: '..the finest fattening land in the Kingdom'.These areas too, were the breeding ground of the mosquito that spread 'The Ague', (malaria).

The increasing popularity of the Marsh awakened enthusiasm in the inhabitants for greater communal efforts toward land-drainage reforms. The population was increasing and farmers banded together to utilise their employed labour to maintain banks and sewers in the winter, when there was little for the men to do, and thorn and hazel faggots were being tried as land drains and tidal reclamation works. Wildfowl was being over-caught, as demand in the towns increased, so in 1534, an Act was passed prohibiting the destruction of wildfowl and taking of eggs between May and August. The Fenmen were the original conservationists!

The late sixteenth century also saw the start of Fen shrinkage becoming reclaimable where the peat was shallow, but the Fenmen were not aware of this.

The earliest form of engine for raising water was the horse pump; the horse walking round a yoke beam which was attached to a horizontal paddle wheel in a chamber and the water being forced outward through a channel, or trough, over a small bank. This was in operation by the thirteenth century, but could only raise the water 2 feet at the most. Manually operation gantry pumps, using a bath-shaped bucket, were used to lower the water level in a drain over a small dam into a storage drain. Neither of these tools was able to cope with a flood evacuation.

This situation worsened over the next two hundred years, as the outfalls to the main rivers silted up and cultivated drained silt began to shrink. The wind driven grinding mills of Holland had, by 1350, been converted to raising water successfully; these could grind corn inside the mill in the normal way and drive a side shaft through a rudimentary gear-box to a paddle wheel in a chamber outside.

The 'mills' mentioned in 'Presentments to the Courts of Sewers' in the Fens after 1395 were water-raising engines, erected by wealthy 'Reclaimers', like the Abbots and Barons, to protect their investments. Mills at Thorney and Crowland and in South Holland are mentioned in Court records, but only on siltlands and high clay lands. References to water-raising mills occur frequently in Dutch manuscripts through the fifteenth and into the sixteenth centuries and the new mills in the North Level would certainly have been imported from Holland and erected by Dutchmen. However, not until about AD 1550, was the first British water-raising mill erected. They were known appropriately as Engines, a British word, (not 'Mill'), later as pumping engines. The artificial drainage of the North Level had begun.

The dissolution of the monasteries, in 1539, brought chaos to the region. Much of the land was owned by the Monasteries of Ely, Peterborough, Thorney and Crowland, which were responsible for upkeep of sewers and banks. Their land-holdings were split up and distributed to the Fenmen creating an impossible situation for the Commissioners of Sewers, and intensifying the Fenmen's parochial attitude. The monasterial riches were seized by the Crown, especially the Black Fen, and the resources to maintain embankments, etc. also practically disappeared.

Brine Boiling

16th Century Dutch Scene

Tandem Wind Engines

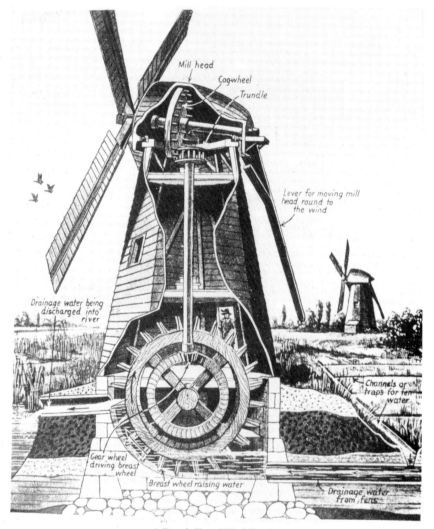

Mill head

Cogwheel

Trundle

Lever for moving mill
head round to
the wind

Drainage water being
discharged into
river

Channels or
traps for fen
water

Gear wheel
driving breast
wheel

Breast wheel raising water

Drainage water
from fens

A Dutch Type Wind Engine

Sir William Dugdale declared that 'the Drowning of the Fens was caused by neglect..'. This was true, apart from parochial schemes, nothing major was done. Massive floods occurred in AD 1570, both tidal and freshwater, 'caused by the melting of great quantities of snow in the Uplands', and some 38,000 acres were under water. The floods of 1947 were caused by melting snow.

In 1571, Commissioners of Sewers reported banks to be in decay and damaged by cattle, but great breaches appeared in Fendyke, (Murrow Bank), and at Bevis Hall, before any work could be done. In 1575, Captain Thomas Lovell was granted a 21 year Patent, 'For draining the marshes with the aid of inventions perfected overseas [Holland]', and by 1588, several engines had been erected in the North Level area. A Commission for Draining the Fens around Clows Cross was formed, followed two years later, in 1579, by a 'Suit to improve the River Nene Outfall'.

From a technological viewpoint, from 1550 to the end of the 16th century, the design of water-raising engines advanced steadily in England; in place of the Dutch design, with the lower body of the mill being of reed wattle and clay, oak was used, elm for the wheels and paddles. Bearings were made of grease-lubricated stone whilst the sails were covered in canvas which could be rolled up when the winds were too strong, although the mill had to be stopped to allow this operation to take place.

Much of the land in Holland had been reclaimed from the sea, and in that reclamation, was very little variation in ground levels, even after shrinkage. Several small pumped areas could be pumped into large storage channels to drain out through a sluice to the sea at low water, engines only being required to raise the water about two or three feet. Upland water was diverted round the flat area along wide channels cut into the higher ground, often requiring only one large embankment on the lower side. These channels were called 'Catchwater Drains'. The 'Roman Car Dyke' was probably primarily a Catchwater, also used for water transportation. Another example at this time was the Catchwater constructed around Romney Marshes in Kent.

In the North Level, ground levels vary considerably, so, therefore, did pumping levels; the engines pumped into main embanked drains, mostly with a long, tortuous path to the sea, with very little fall. Artificial high water levels were produced by pumping, often to the detriment of unembanked land downstream - a chaotic situation which the commissioners were unable to control. There followed a proliferation of private pumping engines discharging into the main sewers, which had deteriorated due to lack of maintenance. These engines worsened matters and records show ever more complaints of 'land being drowned by the nuisance of wind engines'.

The higher lands around Crowland, Thorney and to the North and West of Wisbech were, by 1575, rigorously cultivated, inland areas growing woad for wool-dyeing, this crop having been produced since Roman times, cole seed, for lighting and heating oil used by the new wind grinding mills, Spelt wheat and hulled barley, grown for bread and cattle feed. In 1593, Humphrey Bradley, a Dutchman, submitted his 'Proposal for Draining the Fens' to Lord Burghley, which was not accepted *because* he was a Dutchman.

The newly reclaimed areas around Tydd and Newton could only produce salt-resistant crops such as rape and ryegrass, whereas higher areas around Wisbech, under cultivation longer, yielded greater diversification of crops, including soft and hard wheat as well as, in the prevailing clement weather, vines for wine making. Much of this higher land had rich grass meadows capable of supporting thousands of sheep, while cattle could only be sustained on the siltland, where there were adequate supplies of fresh water in the summer, as water in the drains became too salty when evaporation occurred. Much cattle-raising was in the lower clayland areas bordering high lands to which they could be moved during flooding. More often, the way out from flooded areas was along the banks with subsequent damage caused by poaching.

All this produced the 'final awakening' to the need for solutions to the overall problems and the realisation of Fenmen that it was necessary to invest in drainage works financed with outside capital, in return for giving up ownership of land reclaimed as a result,

Since the Saxon invasion, cultivation had been powered by oxen, a very effective means of draught; they could be bred, trained, used, and when past their best, eaten! Tough or not! By 1066, however, on the continent, horses not selected by the knights for military use were allocated to the land, where it was found that four horses could do the work of eight oxen. Perhaps these too were eaten when worn out - horse-flesh is popular in Europe. Thus emerged the British Agricultural Heavy Horse: the Shire.

Most of the Norman war horses were bred in the marshlands of Holland, Belgium and Germany, their large feet able to support their own weight and that of a fully armoured knight riding in soft, muddy conditions. William of Normandy had defeated the English by using Heavy Horse Cavalry, and, once he and his knights were established, they continued to breed the Heavy Horse, importing both Flemish and

Dutch stallions for the purpose. The Plantagenets continued this policy, and by AD 1171 it is recorded that there was a Horse Sale every Friday at Smithfield in London: 'Here are expensive Chargers of handsome conformation and impressive height, switching their ears and arching their necks, they have massive quarters. When they are run up, the prospective buyers first watch the slower paces then the faster ones, the forefeet are alternatively raised then the hindfeet likewise, a shout goes up to take the common horses aside. Here are Mares for ploughing or draught in sled or double harness cart. Some are heavy in foal, yet others have brought forth their foal which frisk about, their progeny not yet weanable'. At this time oxen were used for heavy cultivation and the draught horse for hauling out the crops on sledges. As a result of Edward's defeat at Bannockburn, an enormous number of great horses were killed or captured, so the Crown issued an edict banning the export of heavy horses to Scotland on 'pain of death', which remained in force for many years.

Selective breeding resulted in the slowest and heaviest being bred in the Fens: so huge were these animals, so large their feet, that they became unsuitable as war horses, but very useful as draught animals, until by 1565, the deteriorating fens could no longer carry them. However, they were in great demand for drawing heavy four-wheeled carriages and were used for the first stage-coaches - another source of income for the Fen farmers. Many of the stallions became pack-horses, whilst mares pulled sledges for moving wool, timber, etc. The breeding of great horses was so successful, that when the Wars of the Roses began, export of the finest to nearby European countries had started extending to Italy. They were also being imported into Scotland by the thousand. Henry III stopped the export of stallions in AD 1532, making it a felony carrying a fine of £40 - a huge sum in those days - whilst, towards the end of his reign, he encouraged the use of castration to weed out the small and weak; obviously no-one informed him how this new-fangled operation worked!

One cannot under-estimate the great horse's importance; these animals enhanced the prosperity of the North Level through the centuries, indeed, most early pumping and water supply depended on them: oxen had to be *driven*, horses could be *trained*.

I have always been intrigued by a wind engine in Holland, built in 1585 and still working; instead of driving a paddle or scoop wheel it drives a modern helical screw pump with a lift of about four feet. The same family have owned it since they had it built, expertise in its operation being handed down from father to son, the present incumbent is 35 years of age. To see and hear it running at full revolutions, with an eighteen to twenty knot wind, is a fantastic experience. Inside, the whole structure shakes and clatters, the engine having to be shut down when the sails reach 95 'ends' per minute, (an end occurs when a sail passes the ground). I have witnessed this, it looks as if everything is going to fly apart, quite frightening when seen for the first time.

A working Dutch Wind Engine now Driving A Helical Screw Pump

Self and Willum turning the Engine to the Wind

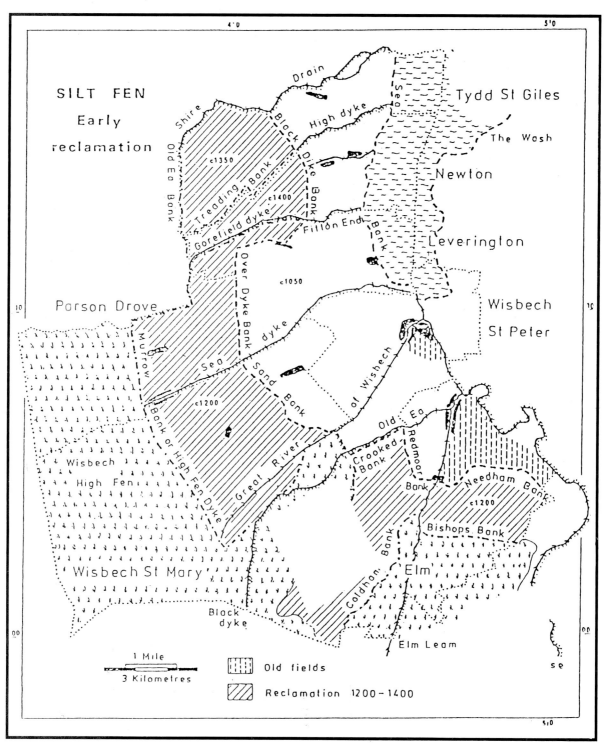

Medieval Settlements, Fields & Flood Banks around Wisbech

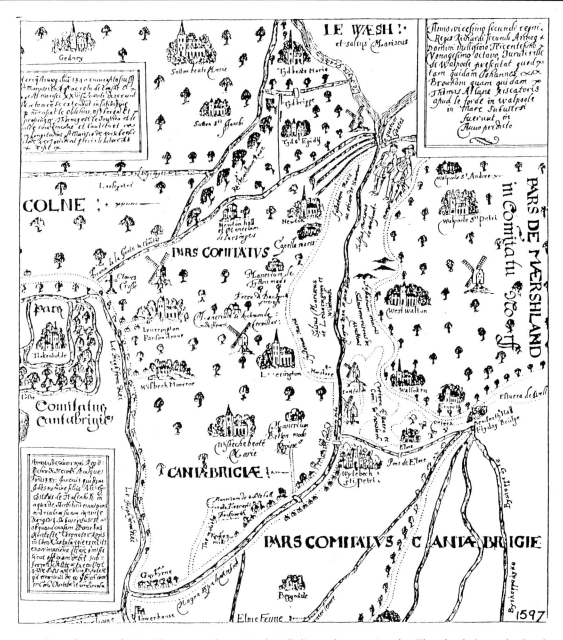

Part of a map of 1597. The text on the original is all directed to proving that Throckenholt, on the South Eau bank, lies in Cambridgeshire and not in Lincolnshire.

Included in the original writing are the following matters:

i) A Grant of Hermitage at TROKENHOLD by Nigel, Bishop of Ely in 1169 and confirmed by Edward II.

ii) In 1274, a commission of knights to decide on county boundaries. Lincoln and Northants could not agree. No sheriff of Lincolnshire ever passed beyond the river South Eau in execution of his duty.

Bottom Left Box. In the eleventh year of the reign of King Richard II and the year of our Lord 1387, a certain young man, John by name, son of Adam Sabyn, the custodian of Trokenhold, sailing on the water of Southes, and carelessly steering his little boat, was drowned. On which account Edward Hyntoft, the King's Coroner in the County of Cambridge made examination of the premises as is duty bound from which it is plain beyond doubt that the marsh of Wisbech lies in the County of Cambridge and not in Lincoln.

Part of a map of 1597 - with translation

DATELINE

CABBAGES & KINGS
Various Landmarks and Bits of Useless Information

Not many people know that in:

1070 Hereward The Wake set up a Camp of Refuge in the Fens, but he eventually submitted to William I, The Conqueror, and the Resistance was finally over by 1072.

1075 The Earl of Norfolk tried a Revolt, but ended up being executed

1086 Doomsday Inquest, the first national census!

1087 William II, Rufus, ascends the throne.

1100 Henry I's marriage to Edith (who changed her name to Matilda at her wedding) - daughter of Malcolm, King of Scotland, united the Saxons and the Normans.

1153 Henry II ascends the throne.

1166 Henry II sets up the Grand Jury system with travelling Judges.

1189 Richard I, The Crusader, ascends the throne.

1190 Wisbech Barton is exempted from taxes in fairs and market to enable the monies to be used to repair the banks.

1199 Richard I is killed in battle and succeeded by John.

1215 John is forced to sign Magna Carta at Runnymede by the Barons.

1223 Henry III confirms Magna Carta on his coming-of-age in 1227.

1226 'Hundreds of Wisbech flooded by Tidal Water. Tide flowed for two days and one night without ebbing, due to a violent wind from the North-East.

1258 First Land Drainage Act sets up Courts of Sewers. Henry II directs that repair work be carried out in Wisbech Hundreds.

1260 'Prodigious' rainfall and high tides combine to cause catastrophic flooding in the Level.

1272 Edward I. Wool Duties granted to the Crown.

1274 Littleport Cut made. River Ouse changes course - away from the River Nene.

1275 Hugh de Bolsham is assigned to the monks of Ely to reclaim the Wisbech High Fen.

1295 Edward I summons the Model Parliament.

1307 Edward II ascends the throne.

1314 Edward II instructs Geoffrey de Colville to view the banks in Newton and Wisbech St Mary, then 'in decay', and repair same.

1332 A further Doomsday Inquest reports that '[the] Fens and Marshes now more wealthy than the Uplands'.

1335 Geoffrey de Colville again instructed to repair the banks in Newton and Wisbech - 21 years later.

1339   The Black Death.

1377   Richard II ascends the throne.

1381   The Peasants' Revolt - Watt Tyler killed. John O'Gaunt's son Henry usurps the throne to become Henry IV.

1406   Parliament re-organised, local government and the privy council.

1413   Henry V ascends the throne.

1427   'Drainage Act' makes the Commissioners statutory.

1429   Henry VI 'The Navigator' ascends the throne. Henry VI orders Sir John de Colville to repair Wisbech Fendyke (Murrow Bank) and cleanse the South Eau to Throckenholt; the Bishop of Ely also ordered to do likewise to the South Eau via Clough's Cross to Guyhirn.

1437   The 'Great Breach' in Fendyke flooded the Northside Area.

1461   Edward IV ascends the throne.

1480   Bishop Morton straightened the River Nene between Guyhirn and Wisbech, cutting through old banks at Mouth Lane and Bevis Hall.

1483   Edward V followed by Richard III ascends the throne.

1485   Henry VII ascends the throne

1509   Henry VIII ascends the throne

1513   'Drainage Act' specifying the 'Terms of Office' of the Commissioners.

1531   'Land Drainage Act'. Henry VIII decrees that '..Commissioners of Sewers and other premises shall be directed in all parts within this area from time to time and when need shall require.....'. Commissioners to serve three years.

1539   Dissolution of the Monasteries.

1553   Mary ascends the throne.

1558   Elizabeth I, 'The Virgin Queen', ascends the throne.

1560   The Market Place in Wisbech raised - using soil from the river bank - higher than the tide level.

1570   A Great Flood recorded after Christmas and attributed to melting snow at Candlemas.
        NB. In 1947 there were floods from the same cause.

1571   Reported that the banks were in a state of decay. A breach occurred in the bank at Bevis Hall before repairs could be carried out. Commissioners' term of office extended to ten years.

1579   'Suit' to improve the River Nene, but no funds available.

1588   First water mills erected in Northside.

1589   Treatise by Humphrey Bradley to drain the Fens.

1596   The Shire Drain improved and opened. (This resulted in the first report to the Privy Council of damage in 1618).

1600   An Act is passed '...for the recovery of many thousands of acres of Marsh and other grounds..', again no capital available.

CHAPTER V

The First Major Improvements: The Seventeenth Century

In 1600, an Act was passed to recover thousands of acres of marshes. Outside capital was attracted, owners prepared to surrender the worst land - and commoners their rights - but agreement was not unanimous. However, many smaller reclamation schemes resulted, and, in 1607, a bill was passed for the 'Draining of Six-thousand Acres' in Waldersea and Coldham.

At this time, the Fen in Newborough was still in its natural state, like those adjacent to the River Nene from Peterborough to Guyhirn; all the water draining into the Catswater, along the South Eau and Shire Drain, to the sea, twenty-seven miles away. However impossible this looks today, the Fen surface then was 6 to 8 feet higher - in some places more - than now. The highlands of clay and gravel at Eye and Oxney drained into the same channel. Part of the Welland still discharged through Crowland to join the North Nene arm - the South Eau. Embankments were on both sides of Catswater, South Eau and along the channel draining Postland, (Great Porsand), the Dowdale bank - this area being embanked on the North by Queen's Bank. However, much of this area in the northern region was shallow Fen.

The area south of Thorney was drained to Gold Dyke along Thorney dyke, on the edge of the Fen, thence to the Wryde and Fendyke, (Murrow), to the Nene at Guyhirn, whilst Wisbech High Fen was still open to tidal flooding. The region north of Thorney was drained by the Wryde from the Catswater to Murrow, also a cross drain to the Old South Eau, known as Gold Dyke. The present area of the North Level to the north of the south Eau drained northwards to the ancient outfall into the Wash via Fleet. The whole stretch between the South Eau/Shire Drain and Leverington Common drained north-eastwards along four main channels to the sea bank at four Gotes.

A main channel took drainage from small embanked areas between Murrow and Wisbech along Seadyke, White Engine and Red Engine Drains, discharging into the tidal river at Horseshoe Corner, Wisbech. Wisbech Northside drained southwards along Rummers Drain into the River Nene at Cold Harbour Corner. The River Nene, (the Great Wisbech River), was embanked between Cold Harbour Corner and Horseshoe Corner in Wisbech; between Guyhirn and Cold Harbour Corner there was a small marshy area subject to tidal flooding.

Around the North Level were many small meres; Gorefield Fen for instance, and low, wet, marshy areas. Some were remains of ancient channels filled with clay, whilst inland they were stagnant fresh water pools, typical of the Fen. Near the tidal channels they were brackish, unsuitable for much growth, but a haven for wildfowl. Concurrently, tidal flow in the major channels had been cut off by the installation of sluices or 'sasse', mostly simple pointing doors with smaller, inset doors in them, allowing them to let out fresh water at neap tides. Many were ineffectual, leaking or blowing out silt under the structure at high spring tides. They all caused considerable silting immediately downstream during periods of little fresh-water flow, creating another major maintenance problem.

Except for the high silt lands around Tydd and Wisbech, and the clay islands around Thorney, Crowland and Eye, much of the region was known as Summer Lands, capable of carrying stock and producing hay, but virtually unusable in the winter, due to freshwater inundations. Tidal floods, because of bank breaches, although sometimes violent, drained away relatively quickly, except for the low area mentioned earlier.

When James I succeeded in 1603, his personal interest encouraged proposals, and various Engineers recommended improvements including; Richard Atkyns and Hayward, whose Map of the Fens was the most accurate. Many disputes rose about the powers of the commissioners of Sewers to make new sewers, their authority did not extend this far, being used previously, only for embankments, 'in times of stress'.

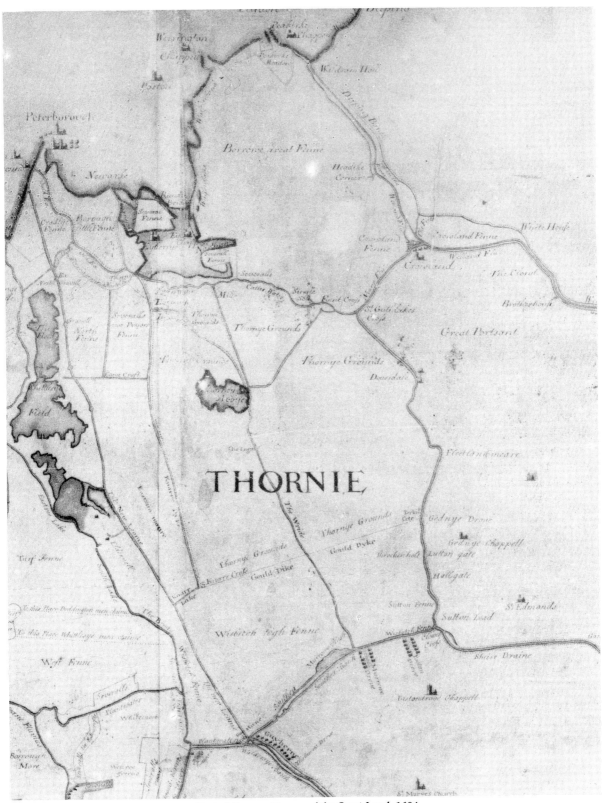

Part of Hayward's map of the Great Level, 1604

The anciently cultivated, prosperous lands around Wisbech focused attention on improving the outfall of the River Nene before other major works were attempted. Works near Upwell had to be abandoned, due to lack of an adequate outfall. Major tidal floods in 1607 and 1613 produced many presentments to the Court of Sewers, thence to the Privy council. Loss of life in the Wisbech area led to Sir Clement Edmunds being instructed to report directly to the Privy Council after inspection of the Fen Defences, with recommendations. He reported that: '[the Great Wisbech River], wanted much in depth and is grown up and choked with silt'. The bed stood six foot higher than before '[and] the sluice erected at Horseshoe below Wisbech had stood but seven days, but was broken and blown up by the tide'. He added 'the Upland men ought to contribute to the scouring of the river which drained their land'. Edmunds, damning criticism of 'Fenmen' runs: 'He that will do any good in serving must do it against the will of such that will profit by it'.

The King, in 1620/21, declared that he himself would undertake major works and Vermuyden was asked to prepare a report. Vermuyden had already done works for the King at Windsor, but in order to finance the new Vermuyden scheme, the monarch required 130,000 acres of Fenland to add to his existing ownership. Nothing was done, most of the land to be surrendered, being Commoners' Land in the Fen. After James' death in1625, Charles I was uninterested and pushed advancement onto his subjects. There followed several Presentments to the Courts of Sewers, with suggestions for financing of major works. One was a 'charge' on all drained land.

In 1628, the Commissioners of Sewers at Ely proposed a contract with Vermuyden, but received so many objections against a 'foreigner' receiving compensation for work on their, (Fenmen's), land that the plan was dropped. Nevertheless, between 1626 and 1628, Vermuyden drained Hatfield Chase, financed entirely by Holland. He was an 'Undertaker', (Contractor), not an 'Adventurer', (Entrepreneur), and was knighted by the King as a result.

Things deteriorated so fast in the Fenland that land owners met and talked and finally asked the Duke of Bedford's help, as owner of 20,000 acres in the Thorney area. He accepted the challenge, to drain the Bedford Level within six years; his recompense 95,000 acres, with 40,000 acres set aside for future maintenance.

The contract, 1630, known as the 'Lynn Law', was followed by the 'Indenture of Fourteen Parts', resulting in the Duke and his Adventurers receiving Royal Charter of Incorporation in 1634. The Duke overcame local prejudice against Vermuyden, and his proposals were accepted, work commencing in the North Level. Vermuyden was not only the Contractor, but also an Adventurer, one of the Entrepreneurs.

Vermuyden decided to split the Great Level into three parts:-
(i)   The North Level from the Glen to the Nene
(ii)   The Middle Level from the Nene to the Bedford River
(iii)   The south Level - the remaining area to the South

From 1634 to 1636, Vermuyden, (whose contract was to produce Summer Land), carried out the following works in the North level:-

1. Straightened Morton's Leam a mile and a half downstream from Peterborough and improved the rest of the Channel.
2. Cut Peakirk Drain from the Fenn near Peakirk to Guyhirn, 10 miles long, 17 feet wide.
3. Improved Straight Reach and Shire Drain to the outfall with a new outfall structure at Hill's Sluice.
4. Cut a new channel, known as the New South Eau - from the Catswater, near Crowland, to Clough's Cross, erected a new sluice there to control flood water.
5. Reported to have renewed the sluice at Horseshoe with a great stone structure, but I can find no details of this, or how long it lasted. It probably survived two or three years, as only by mid-nineteenth century did engineers begin to understand problems of Silt. This sluice would have underblown and collapsed like many dams in the past - and as many would do in the future.

In 1637, at a Session of Sewers at Ely, it was adjudged that the late surrounded grounds in the North and Middle Levels had been drained according to the true intent of the 'Lynn Law', but this adjudgement was obviously premature and a means of restoring the fortunes of the Adventurers. Such a spate of complaints and petitions regarding the exchange of land for incomplete works ensued that, in 1638, the King decided the award of 95,000 acres should be withdrawn as the undertakers had not fulfilled the contract.

The Lynn Law allowed for improvements for Summer Lands, but this did not satisfy the Fenmen deprived of land, wanting protection from winter floods. The King then declared himself the Undertaker and made a further contract with Vermuyden, who reported privately to the monarch - work began again. Vermuyden's report, The Discourse, was publicly released in 1642. Crucially, the contract was made to produce Winter Land, ie protection against winter floods.

This second phase of improvement again commenced in the North Level:

1. The Wisbech River was straightened and confined in about 1638, from Horseshoe to Rivers' End, no mention made of the Sluice at Horseshoe. Elstobb quotes that workmen found the old stone bed of the river some eight feet lower.
2. Vermuyden constructed the Barrier Bank on the North and South sides of Morton's Leam, from Stanground to Guyhirn, with a new sluice at Stanground to divert the Nene waters. Also a lock with two flash doors and a pound at the 'Dog in a Doublet', the new channel to give water transport from Thorney Dyke to Peterborough, in order to serve the Thorney area via Morton's Leam.
3. Further work was completed to Shire Drain.
4. Further work was done on Wryde Drain and Peakirk Drain.

The North Level, being mainly marsh, benefited immediately from the new straight channels, which increased the flood capacity due to better gradients, and particularly in the areas furthest from the sea. Having a relatively small portion of Fen, the area escaped many rebellious Riots of the Middle Level from the inhabitants, although a leader and landowner emerged from their midst, named Cromwell. He, although a Squire from Huntingdonshire, was basically responsible for the demise of the great works, being carried out under extreme difficulties. Many Fenland Reclaimers were persuaded to join Cromwell's adventurism imagining, mistakenly, that his Protestant Crusade would better the lot of the common man. Instead ignorant peasants were simply cannon fodder, doomed to be killed or maimed in Cromwell's battles. It took nearly a generation after the foundation of the Commonwealth for many to recover their holdings, and lack of sons to continue their family lines caused a vast number to fail. I believe Wentworth Day was absolutely correct in his comment: 'Cromwell, that self-righteous, Bible-punching Dictator, the Hitler of his day, cultivated assiduously the support of the Fenmen and influenced their ignorant minds against the Crown and Gentlemen Adventurers; he created for himself the tawdry title of Lord of the Fens, but did nothing towards draining them. 'This Regicidal Huntingdonshire Squire, who contributed nothing to the goodness or greatness of the country, other than spill most of its best blood in battle and die with murder on its soul, left behind a legacy of Puritanical Humbug which imbued some Fenmen with his own spirit of religious cant on Sundays and sharp dealing on weekdays.'

Religious acrimony among the larger farmers was still apparent in the North Level in the nineteenth century, employees were forced to attend private chapels, morning and evening, although living in conditions of squalor. Many of these landholdings can be traced back to Cromwell's time, both Royalists' and Roundheads' fortunes fluctuating.

The Civil War, from 1642 until the King's execution in 1649, gave Fenmen the opportunity to undo much successful drainage work already carried out. The Fenland reverted, in 1650, to its earlier sorry state. However, the fifth Duke of Bedford agreed to restore and further improve the Great Level - Vermuyden was his undertaker, and work commenced on the North Level. The third stage of works included the following:-

1. Cutting of the counter drain from Peterborough to Guyhirn and raising of the North Barrier Bank from Peterborough to Guyhirn, which completed the tidal embankment through Wisbech High Fen.
2. Completion of the embankments from Guyhirn to Wisbech.
3. Raising and strengthening the South Barrier Bank of the Welland from Peakirk to Brotherhouse Bar.
4. Shire Drain cleansed and improved.

Other improvements were also carried out by the Corporation, where petitions were made for the Fen, particularly adjacent to the River Nene. These works were completed in 1651, the rest of the great level finished by 1653, when the Adventurers took possession of their land, the Duke of Bedford mostly in the North Level, around the area he already owned at Thorney, extending eastwards to Gold Dyke, northwards to the Old South Eau.

In 1651, the Duke had the banks raised around his holding ensuring that, if flooding occurred, it wouldn't come over his side! These banks remained until his land was sold in 1910; some, like the Old South Eau, still standing, doubtless because of his policy of building a road on top of the bank. Many were improved and his tenants were required to keep their drains clear and in good repair, the Duke initially paying for upkeep of the main banks and drains until the Incorporation Act of 1667, when the Bedford Corporation took responsibility. The Duke's agent became Collector of Taxes and Expenditor in the North Level, therefore monies spent on maintenance were probably directed to the protection of the Duke's Estate. The increased prosperity in the North Level was phenomenal, many droves were hardened by imported stones, new farmhouses built on the estate, new churches erected, (always a sign of wealth), and wagons, pulled by shire horses, gradually superseded water transport.

The following extract from The English Improver Improved, (1652), explaining agricultural reform, categorises the agricultural land resulting from the Great Drainage Scheme:-

'1.   Land seldom or never flooded should be pastured and sown with hemp, woad, or even madder.

'2.   Land occasionally flooded, might ultimately be proved to be the best, sew cole seed and exceeding rich for all types of grain.

'3.   Lowest land of all, turf or bog, little use except common land, to be turfed, hassocks cut out and over-turfed, pared up, put in heaps and burnt, then spread and sew cole seed...'

Hemp, grown for rope for the Navy, was also dried, ground and made into cannabis by the local inhabitants, doubtless to relieve the Ague, but also, because of their appalling living conditions, their existence was only bearable by being 'high as a kite' most of the time. Cole seed, ground by the oil mills like the one remaining at Wisbech, provided heating and lighting and was the forerunner of Rape seed, a standard crop yielding oil today.

The seventeenth century saw the emergence of the Land Drainage Engineers like Vermuyden, Westerdyke, Dodson, Lord George Critchley, Kinderley, Atkyns, Lovell, Burrell and Edmund. There were also Dike Reeves and Drainage Commissioners, who had learned their craft from years of success and failure on the ground, forerunners of the present-day Drainage Board Members.

Vermuyden's major contribution in the field of land drainage, was his realisation that the full spring flood tide reduced the freshwater flow and thereby its gradient, this increasing water levels. His answer was to make an artificial sump or receptacle, where the rise in water would be limited by enabling the freshwater to spread over a large area, embanked on either side. He first created the Whittlesey Washes, part of the Welland Washes, and largest, the Ouse Washes, all maintained as an integral part of the flood protection design to this present day; this principle of Flood Control Washes, pioneered first in the North Level, has been used throughout the world. To appreciate Vermuyden's achievement, the difficulties faced need explaining.

The new channel, often through wet land, had to be dug by hand; mostly using wooden spades, (or sloughs), adapted from peat cutting tools, some with a metal sheathed cutting edge, for clay; some long and thin, for cutting peat and silt; others with a bowl shaped head and long handles for jack balling.

The first cut was made 2 to 3 feet deep, depending on the wetness; each clod being passed to the jack baller, then thrown clear of the limit of the channel; this material often being moved a second time. The next 'bite', again of about 2 feet, often had to be barrowed, as it was too wet to jack ball. This material, placed at the back of the spoil heap, was allowed to drain. The cut came out in short lengths and water draining into it was continually bucketed out over a dam. The barrows were wooden, the planks narrow and slippery. The men's boots were leather, liberally covered with goose grease or tallow, with spikes strapped to them.

Vermuyden brought much skilled labour, mostly Huguenots and Walloons, (the Protestant reformers of the time), from Northern France, Belgium and Holland. The Walloons were expert land drainage workers and artisans, the Huguenots were farmers and men of substance - entrepreneurs. These formed the nucleus of the workforce, most settling in Thorney, later in Parson Drove and Guyhirn.

The unskilled labour force comprised some 500 Dutch sailors, captured by Captain Blake, plus 10,000 Scots, captured at the Battle of Dunbar in 1650. Only strong, single, willing men were wanted, the majority were marched from York, taken to the North Level, clothed and booted, then settled in primitive camps. They reached the working sites by walking along the new banks or by boat. Often paid in arrears, they had to live off the land by fishing and poaching, etc., buying essential foods locally when in funds.

The prodigious amount of channel excavation completed in this manner is difficult to imagine when scrutinising the works carried out, especially as little, except perhaps the topcut, could be done in winter. As well as this channel work, spoil heaps were formed into embankments for access, bridges and sluices were constructed by artificers, (construction workers). Many of these access banks and bridges became Toll Roads after the 1663 Act.

Sad to relate, after all this display of inventive genius and the works completed under his guidance, Sir Cornelius Vermuyden died a pauper. It is utterly shameful that a lasting monument to his genius as a great, seventeenth century engineer, has not been erected in the Fenland. This is a project that should be taken up by the landowners and drainage authorities in the Fens who are beneficiaries of his work.

When the North Level First Major Improvement was completed, conditions improved dramatically, with a reduction in winter inundations and increased protection from the sea; but the problem of siltation remained and even accelerated adjacent to the sluices, worsening due to lack of freshwater floods over a few years. Vermuyden's Sluice, erected in 1649 on Shire Drain, silted, and a new one, Gunthorpe Sluice, further downstream, was erected in 1652. Siltation affected all outfalls, especially where sluices were erected. Engineers did not understand the effect of blocking an existing tidal channel, and many of these had to be dug out each year before the winter.

Further problems occured on the banks built in the Fen; the material for these was obtained by cutting a new channel alongside as previously described. This local material was mainly peat mixed with silt which could be trodden in when the water content was right and then retained water. However, after two or three dry years, the peat dried out and shrunk, losing its water retaining properties, causing seepage during high water levels and eventual collapse. Not until the early eighteenth century was it realised that a core of 'puddled' clay was needed to keep them watertight. This operation meant that a trench was cut along the centre of the bank and shored up with timber. Clay from the brickpits arrived by boat and the trench filled in layers, each layer being trampled by bare feet, (puddled), usually by the men's wives. In Somerset, in 1947, wives were paid 6d an hour for this.

There were still many low areas, numerous small meres and stagnant pools in the region. It was a struggle for the folk to exist. However, a living could be made from the meres. Ducks were often driven from Mere to Mere, the fringes yielded reed and rushes for thatching, peat fern, (New Zealand Flax), willows and osiers for basket making. Many kept flocks of geese, known as Fenman's Treasure, these were plucked live for down or sold for consumption. A Fenman's dowry was often three score geese and a pelt, (a sheepskin coat). It was said that 'willows will buy the owner a horse,before that by any other crop, he can pay for his saddle'. Fish still abounded and wild duck were netted; many wild birds provided food, including the pheasant, introduced to this country by the Romans, its natural habitat being marshland. In 1663, Samuel Pepys, recalling in his diary, his visit to relations in Parson Drove, comments: 'The poor wretches in a sad thatched cottage, like a poor barn, peeling of hemp in which I did give myself good content to their manner of preparing hemp'.

Dugdale, on his Inspection a few years earlier, had written: '[the] Thorney bordering the Fen, but the Fen how environing it are by the Adventurers more so dry that these able all sorts of corns and grass now growing thereon in the greatest plenty imaginable'. The Act of 1667 consolidated the Charter of Incorporation of the Bedford Level, detailing the responsibilities of that august body, and laying down ten grades of taxes related to the quality of the soil and, therefore, the productivity of all land within their control. The eastern area of the North Level was still administered by the Court of Sewers, which only collected Acre Taxes irrespective of productivity. Just before this Act, the Corporation commissioned a survey of conditions in the Level from one Colonel Dodson. His report concluded: 'if we cannot master the problems of the outfalls there, all other endeavours signify nothing'.

He also raised the problem of the wasting peat and lowering ground levels, by stating that beds of the new channels through the Fen were not rising, rather that the land was shrinking. He was right about shrinkage, but not about rising beds. We know that the channel bed through peat land will rise by up to 4 feet in one year. In the Somerset Level, forty-five years ago, the bed had to be dug out every summer, giving rise to spoil heaps 6 feet high which virtually vanished by the following year, this peat being 95% water.

There are several accounts of Journeys through the Fens, printed in the latter part of the century. All find the Fenmen ignorant, rude and slothful, but none of the writers showed any appreciation of the conditions these people endured and the efforts they made to overcome the elements. Their continuous struggle to protect and preserve their lands from the ravages of sea and flood was proof they were not slothful, and, understandably, had scant opportunity for small talk and graciousness in their lives.

In 1695, numerous petitions were made to the Corporation to protect land and houses affected by water inundation. The silt lands around Wisbech and Tydd were mostly able to keep out the sea and the freshwater floods, as their embankments consisted of cohesive material and remained watertight in dry periods. It is recorded that: 'the pasture belt, lying towards the sea very fertile feeding a great number of fat Oxen and Sheep which weekly are sent to London in droves producing wool and tallow as well as meat'.

As Darby comments: 'The Great Drainage which started with promising enterprise ended in tragedy by the end of the century'.

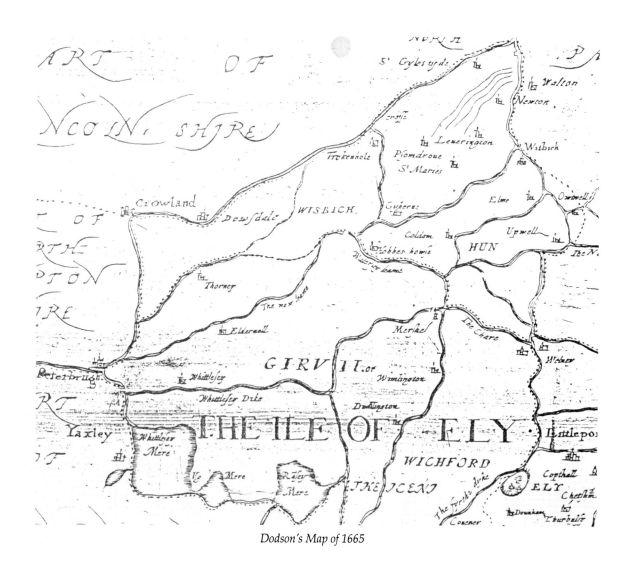

Dodson's Map of 1665

CHAPTER VI

The Wind of Change in the Eighteenth Century

By the eighteenth century, the wind of change in the North Level was blowing exceeding strong, driving the sails of many pumping engines, from small private ones to larger ones erected from the public purse. At this time, the Great Porsand and the area bounded in the north by the Old South Eau, in the south by Mortons Leam reaching from Peterborough to the Murrow Bank, was administered by the Bedford Commissioners under the 1667 Act. The remainder of the region was still controlled by the Hundreds of Wisbech Court of Sewers, and East Elloe Court of Sewers, (Sutton St Edmunds area, north of the South Eau).

The windmills, driving paddle wheels for raising water, originated in Holland in 1344, and the Court of Sewers mention 'engines' in 1555. Many mills, (wind engines), appear on Haywards map of 1604.

Between 1575 and 1592, petitions had been put to the Privy Council for patents for wind engines to drain the Fens by Morrice, Goldhings, Houghseter, Maston and Carleten and we know that engines were then working on Red and White Engine drains and Rummers.

In 1617, it is recorded that an engine was operating at Leverington.

The early mills raised the water only 2 to 3 feet, dependent upon the size of the paddle wheel, the bigger the wheel the greater the lift, but the greater the power to drive it. At first the mill was fixed, pointing in the direction of the prevailing wind, but developed into a central mounted column supporting the structure, with double or triple brace timbers running on rollers, which could be wound by pulleys to point the paddles into the wind.

The largest engines could lift the water 4 to 5 feet, but needed six to eight vast wind vanes to drive the wheel, requiring wind velocities of 8-10 mph, not always available in the Fens.

The small steering paddle wheel, at right angles to the wind direction, which automatically moved the head of the mill carrying the main paddles, was seldom used for engines in the UK, due to lack of wind and paddle wheel resistance, but was seen in grinding mills.

Many engines, both private and public, created more difficulties when erected over sewers, causing increased water levels down-stream and flooding neighbours' land.

The Laws of the Bedford Level enabled the Commissioners to take action only when engines acted as dams in a main sewer, then to have only the obstruction to flow removed, not the whole mill.

Where mills were built on private land discharging into main sewers, the Commissioners could not act even though localised flooding occurred. The sewer under their control had to be locally improved to take the flow. One mill was erected in Tydd St Mary Fen in 1663, and the owner resisted all efforts to have it removed. The Bedford Commissioners, records show that there were fines for causing nuisance or removing blockage for 44 Wind Engines and 37 Horse Mills between 1700 and 1708. However, a new source of power appeared: in 1713, Newcomen invented the steam operated piston, developed into commercial use in 1766, followed by James Watt's rotive engine in 1782.

Despite the expense, the Fen farmers and Drainage Commissioners must have rejoiced, realising that they would no longer have to depend on the vagaries of the wind to keep the land dry.

The increase in engines made small areas even more parochial, especially outside that of the Bedford Commissioners. With more pumping, both Marsh and Fen were shrinking by the century's end, many regions benefiting from one engine, now needed two or three. At Rummers Mill in Wisbech Northside, there were six, and four on Red Engine Drain at Wisbech.

The problem of bank upkeep on the rivers and channel maintenance of sewers became more important and expensive. In 1701, John Reynolds, the Duke of Bedford's steward for the North Level estate,

A Progression of pumps in the Fens, from Wind to Steam and Finally Electrical

informed the Bedford Corporation that "the money allotted this year for works on the North Level is not sufficient to put the works in a defensible condition against an ordinary flood that may happen".

Pressure by landowners in the North Level, (which although the smallest level, contained the greater part of the Duke of Bedford's estate, resulting from the recompense of the Great Drainage of the Fens), to have control of their own finances increased as they were not getting an adequate return on the taxes paid to the Corporation.

Drainage in the Bedford area of the North Level was still dependent on the outfall at Guyhirn and Gunthorpe Sluice on the Shire Drain. Both outfalls continued to silt and the bed of the Wisbech river still rose.

In 1715, the Corporation commissioned a survey of the Wisbech River outfall by Kinderley, who recommended confining, straightening and further embanking the river from River End to St Peter's Point, about seven miles downstream from Wisbech. This proposal would relieve both Gunthorpe Sluice, (shire drain), and Fourgotes, (Leverington, Gorefield and Newton). It was commenced in 1721, stopping in 1722, when the Corporation ran out of money. They had assumed that people of Wisbech and the Hundred of Wisbech Court of Sewers would contribute, starting work without this agreement; such was the Bedford Commissioners' autocratic attitude. In 1728, a major channel was cut from Peterborough to Guyhirn on the North side of the washes by Smith, a respected Conservator of the Bedford Corporation, in anticipation of further works being carried out to the Nene outfall. This channel had the effect of discharging the upland water more quickly to the sea. In the process, the North Barrier Bank was raised and a small cradge, (bank), built along the washes.

A new lock was constructed at the Dog in a Doublet and the channel upstream extended to Thorney to connect with Peakirk Drain, (Old Wryde), enhancing the water transport system of the Duke of Bedford's estate.

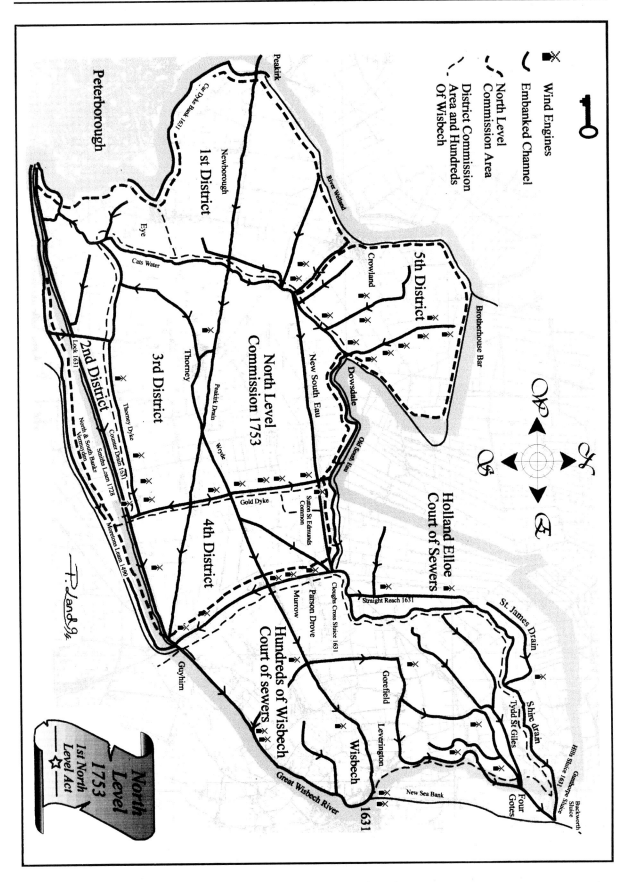

A Map of the North Level, 1753

This was the era of tolls; estate records of 1704 show a substantial income from tolls from the Dog in a Doublet Lock. The droves and tops of the main banks were hardened with imported stone, toll houses blossomed on the main transport routes at Guyhirn, Thorney, Eye and the Welland and Nene Banks. The National Rivers Authority is still required to maintain a hard track on the Welland and Folly River banks from Peakirk to Crowland and along the Nene Bank from Fengate to Storey's Bar Tollhouse.

Fifty years of petitions to the Privy Council ensued and legal actions cost both Wisbech and the Corporation large sums which could have been spent on the works. Many reports were discussed, but nothing was done. To give you some idea the following is a list of reports submitted to the Corporation:

Nat Kinderley	1720
John Grundy	1728
Brigadier Robert Hunter	1728
Humphrey Smith	1726
Captain Parry	1726/27
Nathaniel Kinderley Junior	1751
William Elstobb	1767
Edward Langley	1771
Richard Dunthorne	1771

Nat Kinderley's proposals of 1720, updated by his son, were finally accepted and the new confined and embanked channel was completed in 1773, enabling a new Gunthorpe sluice and sluice-keeper's house to be constructed on the shire drain, also a new Buckworths sluice taking the water from Four Goates. Success at last. These works also enabled a new drain to be cut diverting the water from the South Holland and East Elloe Court of Sewers to a new outfall to the River Nene in 1795-6.

The North Level Drainage Acts of 1753 set up an independent Commission separate from the Bedford Corporation, which was followed in 1754 by the Nene Navigation Act setting up the Nene Outfall Commission.

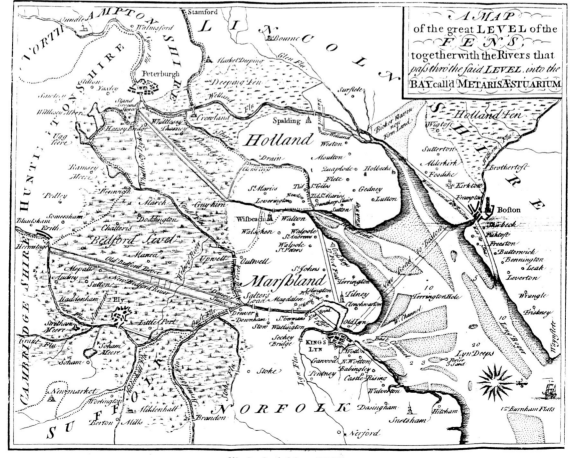

Kindersley's Map of 1724

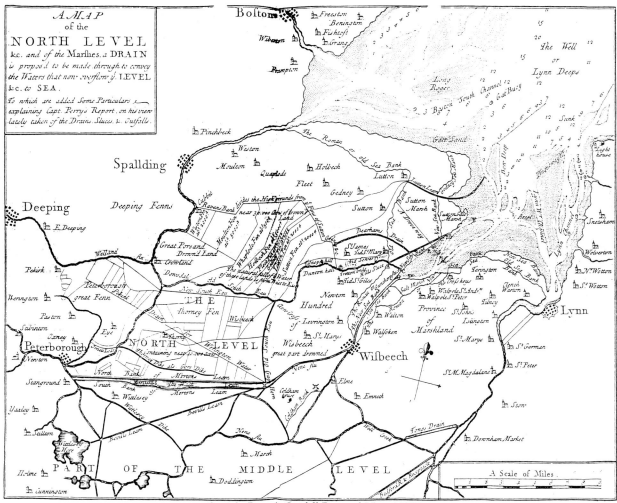

Captain Perry's Outfall Proposal Map of 1726

The North Level Act set up five separate Districts each with its own Committee of Commissioners responsible for the area's drainage, each district to raise a rate, payable to the North Level Commissioners, for upkeep of main sewers and embankments which carried district water to the sea and their own internal drainage.

The Duke of Bedford and Earl of Lincoln, the principal recipients of land from the Great Draining, were required under the Act to pay the return from some 40,000 acres to the Bedford Corporation for maintenance, but because the Act limited the taxes which could be levied, the income was insufficient to cover maintenance costs. The Corporation debts rose, until by 1753 the Corporation costs had been subsidised by the above land owners to the tune of £18,915. Under the North Level Act, £1,800 was required to be paid by the North Level, the remainder of the Corporation's debt being written off by the Duke and Earl in return for the removal of the liability to contribute to maintenance costs except for normal owners' financial tax commitment.

So the North Level Act set up the administration without the burden of excessive debts.

The Second North Level Act of 1771 empowered Commissioners to raise loans limited to £5,000 for excessive works, ie the repair of major breaches, and raised the limit of taxes to be paid by the tenants, but allowed them to deduct these amounts from the Rack rent, a rent paid for land and building during a tenancy, as opposed to an annual usage rent, (hired land). This act also appointed a Receiver of Taxes for the North Level, who just happened to be the Duke of Bedford's steward for his estates in the North level! More of this later!

By this time the 'wind of administrative change" was blowing a gale. In 1773 came the 2nd District Act, 1775 the Wisbech Northside Act, 1798 2nd 4th District Act, 1880 the Leverington and Parson Drove Act, 1809 the Sutton St Edmund Act.

By the end of the Eighteenth Century the North Level Area was administered by several independent Drainage Commissions, successors to the various Courts of Sewers, each with a right to raise taxes

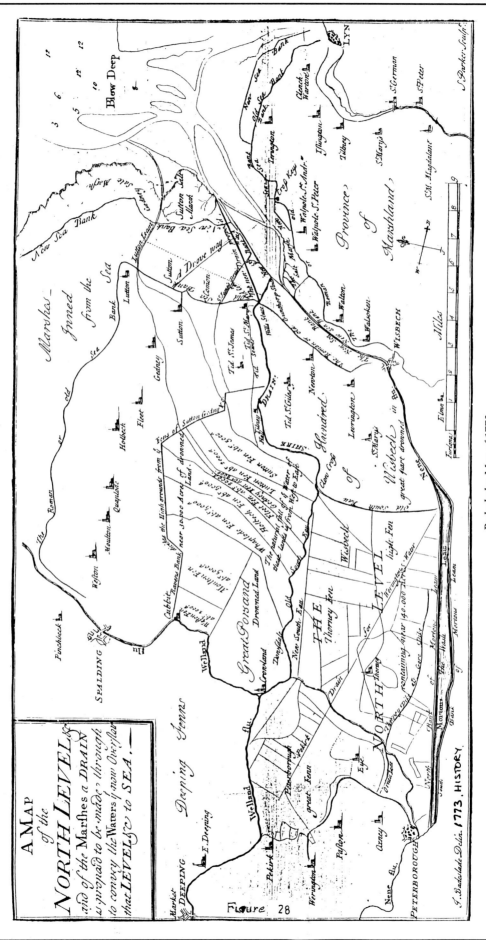

Figure 28

Badeslades Map of 1773

and limited loans: further laws being enacted when the need arose for major expenditure for improvements.

Interestingly, within the area of 97,000 acres there was one small part still 'private' inasmuch as it was still 'bog' - Gorefield Fen.

Minute and Order books for the various Drainage Commissions contain much information, but unfortunately several old books have been purloined and sold for gain by unscrupulous persons when administrative changes occurred. However, to the everlasting credit of successive North Level Administrators, their records have been preserved and are safely in the hands of the County Archivist at Cambridge.

Under the 1753 Act, the North Level Commissioners were responsible for defined main sewers, (from now on called Drains), and embankments, the District commissioners being accountable for the internal drainage of the district, local drains and pumping engines. John Wing's map of his survey of 1749 is the definitive map of the administrative boundaries of the drainage districts in the North Level and the major drains taking water to the sea.

The First District drained eastward along Peakirk Drain, several internal drains to the Catswater and thence to the New South Eau. The Second District drained partly along the Catswater, Thorney Dyke and the Counter Drain, but generally along the latter. The Third District's southern part drained along Thorney Dyke to Gold Dyke, thence along the New South Eau, the northern part drained along Peakirk Drain, Wryde Drain and Gold Dyke to the New South Eau. The Fourth District's southern part drained via the Counter Drain and Peakirk Drain to the Murrow Bank at Guyhirn, the northern part drained via Wryde drain and the newly cut 16 foot Drain, (now called the New Wryde), to Cloughs Cross.

The Fifth District was drained via internal Drains and along Dowdale Bank to the Old south Eau to Cloughs Cross, much of the internal water being pumped by Windmills.

The north side area of the Hundreds of Wisbech Commission of Sewers consisted of Tydd and Newton, Leverington and Parson Drove, and Wisbech Northside. Sutton St Edmunds was still in the Holland Elloe commission as the area drained northwards, although Gorefield Fen remained independent.

The area was drained in the north by Tydd St Giles Drain and Newton Drain, both falling into the Buckworth Drain, cut early in the century to the sluice on the New Embankment. Leverington, (north), discharged through Leverington Drain with Parson Drove water; some of the area's waters passing along Whit Engine Drain to Wisbech. Murrow and Northside both drained southward via Bellamy's Bridge to Cold Harbour Corner and Rummers mill. An element of Northside near Wisbech drained to White Engine Drain and into the river at Wisbech.

The records for the Wisbech Hundred Court of Sewers had been kept in damp, airless conditions in Wisbech Museum's cellars: many books were welded together, so only a few were readable. However, some interesting records emerged applicable to the Parts of the Hundreds:

August 23, 1704: the charge for erecting a new sluice at Gunthorpe and scouring Buckworth Drain to be laid on the owners of "Neuton and Tid" Fens and on the highland in the Neuton and Tid parishes (note the spelling).
June 14, 1713: Petition by John Creed, owner of 17 acres in Newton Fen that he had never received any benefit and that rates were more than the rent and requesting that draining improvements should be carried out - petition granted.
May 27, 1714: Report that Buckworth Drain was very much out of repair and wholly rendered useless by late Tempest at Sea and the rage of a violent tide ensuing thereon. Ordered that sluice be rebuilt and charged to owners of Leverington, Leverington Parson Drove, Tid and Neuton Fens.
May 31, 1716: Sigmund Trafford and other petitioned that their Fenlands in Tid St Giles Fen suffer from waters of Leverington and Leverington Parson Drove and other places with great quantities of water being continually poured up these Fens which are in great measure, became a Sink or common receptacle of Foreign Waters. Petitioners' prayer that bank may be enlarged and heightened. Ordered that Bank in Levering and Gorefield Fen be heightened so as to keep waters within themselves.
August 2, 1715: Petition regarding dependence of the area on Buckworth Sluice.
June 27, 1717: Report that Buckworth Sluice too high and too narrow. Ordered new Sluice.
January 12, 1719: Buckworth Sluice repaired.
September 28, 1721: Report that Buckworth Sluice in danger of being blown.

The problem of structures in Fen silt was still not understood, as I mentioned earlier. A large tidal Head with low fresh water would blow silt out from under the structure.

Further extracts from the Order Books of the Court of Sewers are as follows:-

May 20, 1673: *Ordered that Drains being very defective in many places thereof for want of 'roading' to the great Hundred of the passage of water.* (This is the first recorded name for weedcutting).

June 1704: *Jury ordered to view Wisbech Northside to improve drainage by erection of a new mill.* (New Mill Engine approved 23rd June).

June 20, 1717: *Order that Bevis Hall Sluice be locked to prevent illegal use.* (People would let the tide in when the elvers (young eels) were running in the spring).

June 4, 1730: *Report of a view on Wisbech Northside which was found to be very wet and the greatest part under water, and that the two present engine mills were not adequate. Ordered that two new engine mills be erected at Bevis Hall and drains made for conveying water to the said mills.*

April 20, 1748: *Reported that the Engine Mills were not dealing with Floodwater. Ordered that the North Bank from Barton Road to Guyhirn be raised and from Guyhirn to Cloughs Cross.*

August 1763: *Loans made to repair bank from Guyhirn to Wisbech after disastrous floods in 1762 and remove old sluice at Bevis Hall.*

January 21, 1764: *Reported that highland floods surrounded Murrow and Northside but the new banks held. It was noted that the country in Wisbech Northside was in a 'melancholy state'.*

November 3, 1772: *Court petitioned that Rummers Sluice was in danger of blowing up. Engine Miller summoned before Court.*

All these works were financed by levying a tax called an acre shot on owners, irrespective of the productivity of the land or how it was drained. The Court of Sewers, or rather, the Dyke Reeves, had problems collecting these taxes. In 1770 it was reported that 'Great monies' were outstanding for repairing Murrow Bank. Owners who embanked their land and pumped the water out, often to the detriment of neighbouring land, were excused payment!

It will be recalled that the Court of Sewers was only empowered to carry out new works "In time of great need" and were limited to the loans they could raise, but the extracts indicate the constant battle against rising tides and freshwater floods and the slow, insidious silting of the gravity outfalls. For instance, Wisbech Northside had by now only one semi-effective outfall; water being evacuated by engines which worked only when the wind blew at 8 mph or more. Peat areas were shrinking!

Not only were Fenmen trying to keep their land dry, so were landowners in the great glacial valleys of the Nene and Welland and their tributaries, Rivers were being widened and straightened, shoals and obstructions removed, to make grazing lands more viable; the great forests covering the uplands of both river catchments were being systematically felled to produce more ships until there was insufficient vegetation to sponge up the rainfall. With a mainly clay catchment, nearly all the rainfall ran off to the rivers creating bigger and more frequent floods which all overloaded the Fens.

This denudation of the upland forests added to the Fenmen's problems as much as ever-rising tides; small wonder demands were made for the upland to contribute to the costs of maintaining channels and embankments; it took roughly a hundred years for law-makers to recognize the justice of these requests.

The century's final thirty years produced not only administrative changes, but with the new powers, an upsurge of major improvements as well as disasters.

After fifty years of talking, Kinderley's proposals for straightening, confining and embanking the Nene outfall were adapted and the new channel from River's End to Gunthorpe Sluice completed in 1773, (now known as Kinderley Cut). The Tydd and Newton Drainage Act meant the Commissioners contributed toward the cost, with the people of Wisbech. The new entrained channel cleared the outfalls at Gunthorpe and Buckworths and further channel improvements in the North Level followed. Buckworth Sluice was enlarged and lowered and the drain leading to it, carrying the water from Tydd, Newton, Leverington Parson Drove, was improved.

Clough Cross Sluice was lowered, Straight Reach and Shire Drain improved and the 16 foot Drain and Wryde cleaned out.

Following the North Level Acts of 1753 and 1771, and the Nene Navigation Acts of 1754, the Outfall Commissioners and the North Level built several public houses along the bank of the river Nene for bargees, hauling up the river, and employees, who received beer dockets as part of their wages: shades of the 'company store'. One of these pubs was the Dog in a Doublet. The origins of old pub names are often obscure. In this case, the publican was also the lock keeper, District Foreman for the North Level and Decoyman for the Decoy on the washes opposite. The little terrier he used for duck-flushing contracted a skin disease and lost all its hair; his wife made it a leather jacket, hence 'The Dog in a Doublet.

FOOD AND FOWL

From 1650 - 1750, better crops were grown, and farmers became aware of what the land needed to create the right growing conditions; six year rotations were normal and they recognised the necessity for drainage. Much of the silt land was worn out and being put down to hard and soft fruit.

Plug drainage, (see drawing in appendix I), was developed for heavy land, the forerunner of mole drains. Hand-made horseshoe clay tiles were laid by hand and covered by straw or brushwood filters. Toward the end of the century, trenching-ploughs were developed which were mole-ploughs entered into a hand-dug trench, pulling in round clay tiles; the motive force being supplied by a horse-driven winch fixed to the ground.

Farmers discovered that woad was a good crop after grassland, hemp had good fertilising properties and turnips were good for rotation of grassland. Wire-worms were prevalent and treated with soot, an old gardeners' trick. Very few potatoes were grown then.

On tired siltlands, some farmers resorted to cropping rabbits, one buck per 100 acres, 200 couples per acre. In 1777, one Mr Drilby had 1300 acres of warrens and declared that the worst vermin were poachers, who received 15 pence per prime pelt.

Successful drainage had reduced the number of small meres, so many farmers constructed the Dutch Decoys on their badly drained Fen, the first in the area at Borough Fen, Newborough, built in 1653. It was run by the Williams family from 1670, until sold in about 1920. In the 1820's an Act was passed prohibiting shooting two miles upwind and one mile downwind of any decoy. In 1830, one, Smeaton, was prosecuted for disturbing Borough Fen Decoy by shooting. In 1760, decoys were constructed at Leverington, Gorefield and the Dog in a Doublet in the washes.

The decoy was dug out with a central pond and five curved, tapering arms, like a starfish. The arms were covered in an arch of entwined willows, later in steel hoops covered in wire netting. These arches spanned 18 feet at the pond, 3 feet at the head, with a hoop net attached to the end. Six foot high Norfolk reed panels were placed in overlapping echelon along the arms, so ducks could not see the decoyman. Twelve tame ducks, with clipped wings, were kept on the pond and fed daily at the same time at the head of the arm. These were the decoys. As the tame ducks swam the downwind arm of the day the rest followed; a small dog, trained to walk in and out of the panels, appeared momentarily occasionally to the ducks. These brief glimpses of the dog were enough to keep the ducks moving up the arm, but not enough to cause alarm. The decoyman and his mate then showed themselves at the head of the decoy, the ducks panicked and rushed into the net. The draw string was pulled tight and the netful of flapping ducks dragged out onto the bank. The squeamish can rest assured that the ducks were despatched humanely. Decoys were a good source of income, especially as transport to London became easier. Borough Fen recorded a catch of 6,000 in one day. This Decoy is still operating and worth visiting, as it is now owned by the Wildfowl Trust and used for Duck Ringing.

I used to help old Mr Linnet, at Marsh Farm, Dengie, Essex, when his 'old boy' was not available. The most we caught in one run was 96 brace, all sent to London except for a couple. This decoy operated every day in the season.

Sugar Beet, not a popular crop, was first grown in the Fenlands in 1786. The Duke of Bedford's tenants were not allowed to grow either sugar beet or potatoes. They were required to operate a six-year rotation and keep a third of their holdings in grass, to ensure continued fertility of the ground.

In 1794, Charles Vancouver did an agricultural survey of parts of the Level. In Tydd St Giles, he found that the land was good for oxen, if fresh water was available, it was the best sheep grazing area in the Kingdom. Leverington and Newton was hungry silt, over-used for production of wheat and oats. Leverington Parson Drove area drainage was uncertain, but suitable for wheat, oats, hemp, flax, cole seed and turnips. In Wisbech St Mary he met with great jealousy and mistrust.

The higher lands of the Thorney area were good for grazing as was the Good Fen; second quality Fen was good for wheat, oats, cole seed and temporary pasture.

The Driving Dog

Newborough Duck Decoy

The Newborough Duck Decoy ~ 1988

THE DRAINAGE OF SUTTON ST JAMES,
TYDD ST MARY, AND SUTTON ST EDMUND

Prior to the Tydd and Newton Drainage Act of 1773, most of Sutton St James and Sutton St Edmund drained northwards through natural channels through Fleet and thence to the old outfalls of the South Holland at Fleet Gote. The cutting of the New Channel through Sutton St Edmunds by Vermuyden, (Straight Reach), in 1632, gave St Edmund an improved outfall together with Tydd St Mary and Gorefield Fen. These improvements encouraged the Holland Elloe Commissioners to carry out further works, including the erection of wind engines to drain, in particular, St Edmund via Old Mill Drain, (Folleys Cross Drain), to the Shire Drain, (Straight Reach), in the late 17th century.

Around 1700, the owners of lands in Sutton St James and north end of Edmund area made an agreement with Sigmund Trafford, the owner of Tilney field and Denhams, to discharge water into Denhams Drain. This was achieved by cutting a new drain on the North side of Broadgate from New Fendyke to

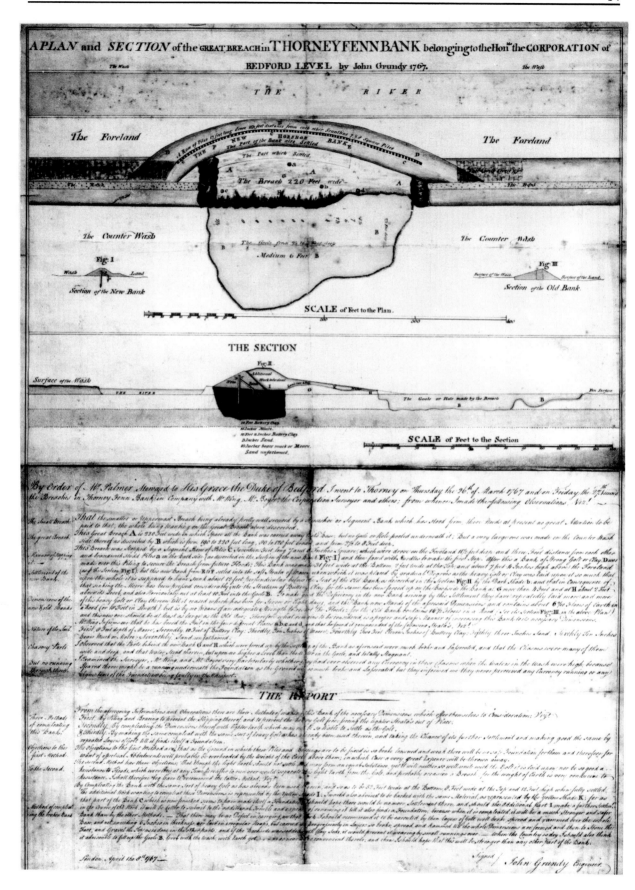

Drawing of a Fen Bank Breach ~ 1767

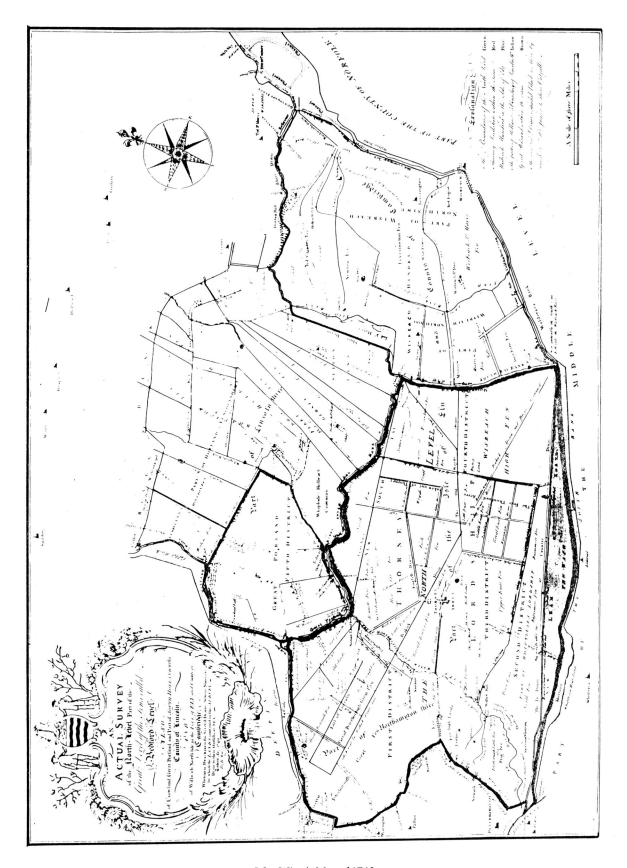

John Wing's Map of 1749

Manor Hill Corner, and erecting a wind engine to raise this water into Denhams Drain and so to Shire Drain. The new drain, known as St James Drain, took water from Sutton St Edmund through a new tunnel under New Fen Dyke.

The agreement was made on 10th December, 1700, between William Hyde, (Gentleman), and Sigmund Trafford, (Gentleman), but on Hyde's death in 1727, the owners of land in Sutton St James bought St James Drain and the engine and made a new agreement with Trafford, which excluded all waters from Sutton St Edmund.

In 1816, a fresh agreement was made between Sutton St James owners and the new owners of Tilney Field to continue the right to discharge waters to Shire Drain. Under the Drainage Act 8, George IV, the owners of lands in Sutton St James petitioned for the permanent right to discharge water to Shire Drain. This was granted in 1838, for £12 per annum, to owners of Tilney Field. This sum is still paid by the North Level to the Lincolnshire country Council, the present owners of Tilney Field.

Redermer Field, on the east side of Sutton St James, still drained to the South Holland Main Drain. It was not until the drainage Order of 1953, which established the Tydd Internal Drainage Board, that half of the Sutton St James area was officially taken into the Authority's area. Previously, the area was administered by Holland Elloe Court of Sewers and Holland Elloe Drainage Board.

Sutton St Edmund's drainage was dependent on the outfall of Straight Reach, and necessitated pumping of the area by wind and subsequently by steam; the first steam pump in the area, until the cutting of the North Level Main Drain in 1832, when flow was reversed southwards.

Disasters mentioned earlier, were a series of major breaches in the North Barrier bank later in the century. These occurred in 1763, 1764, 1767, 1770 and 1773. All these breaches can be seen on the ground today between Peterborough and Guyhirn; they are shown on the Ordnance Survey maps and all are named.

The vital function of the Washes was to reduce flood levels; without these Washes, Peterborough would have suffered major inundation and long lengths of embankment would have collapsed. However, the operation of the Washes can be a two-edged sword should breaches occur, as a vast amount of water is stored at high tide. This will then discharge through the hole and restoration can only be accomplished when water-levels drop sufficiently, which can take as long as three days. The catastrophic effect on crops, livestock, lives and property in the eighteenth century was horrifying.

All the water on the land had to be discharged to the sea at Tydd through drains which were only just adequate to keep normal rainfall from causing flooding. Many areas still required wind engines for sufficient drainage, but these could not operate in flooded conditions.

The task of closing a breach meant all materials had to be transported by boat, including clay, which came from Whittlesey. The ends of the breach had to be secured by wooden piles driven by hand, sealed with faggots and puddled clay. The counter bank, curved toward the river, had then to be constructed from both ends, driving piles by hand in flowing water, cutting down the flow through the piles with straw and faggots, weighted with clay; the ends of each day's work sealed off and secured to prevent them washing away until the work approached the centre of the breach. As the hole became smaller the velocity of the water increased and the scour hole at the back became deeper. Time was of the essence. Men worked at night, with inefficient lighting, in dangerous and wet conditions, usually in winter. Not a job for the faint-hearted. The closing of the breached counter bank was crucial. All materials required for the repair had to be at hand, laid along the existing bank. When the gap was reduced enough to span by timbers, the piles were driven and immediately straw and faggots were dropped from boats on the river side and sucked into the gap. As the water slowed, clay was dropped over the front to be puddled in by poles. When water was reduced to a trickle, the size and depth of the scour-hole at the back could be assessed. This was a crucial stage of the restoration, for unless the temporary piled bank was backed by clay in time for the next rise of water, associated with the high tide, the water would blow out the piled works leading to a new scour-hole and ultimate collapse.

Having backed and secured the counter bank it would now be possible to fill the scour-hole, possibly 16 feet deep, depending on how long the breach had been open. 400 to 500 men were employed on the breach, often for two months.

The catastrophic breaches resulted in the Drainage Commissioners enacting another bill enabling them to raise loans in excess of the original Act's limitation. Between 1795 and 1799, further breaches occurred on the Nene and the Welland Bank. In 1799, 35,000 acres lay underwater.

By the Century's end, the two insidious enemies of the North Level; rising tides with siltation, and shrinking land levels, and several wet years, were taking their toll and farming was ceasing to be profitable, particularly on the Bedford Estate.

EXTRACT FROM THE MINUTES AND ORDER BOOKS

1754 - **4th District** Marshall's of Elm to inspect four mills in the district, one in Bishoplands, one on Cants Drove and two on Adventurers land and to report if these mills are fit to be set up in the District and estimate to move them - ordered two mills to be set up, one at the East End of Bridge Drove, the other at the East end of the Old Wryde, later a third, south of Peakirk Drove at the end of the Counter drain, at £280 each.

1755 - **2nd District** Ordered that Cants mill and Speedwell be moved to make one 14ft wheel mill and one sump mill of 9 ft. dia. (mills required in tandem to lift water into the South Eau)

1756 - **4th District** Ordered that Richard Boyley buys two backs of best oak 36 ft long x 15a x 9a and James Royce puts them up on Murrow Mill and has ready a new sail cloth.

1757 - **North Level** - ordered that the following drains be cleaned and the banks repaired.

1757 - **4th District** Reported that several owners had erected horse mills - ordered to take them down - ordered that land owners scour their own drains

1757 - **4th District** ordered that Parson Drove mill, Murrow mill, Cants mill and Neals Hundred mill be repaired - agreed for two private mills to be erected.

1761 - **North Level** Surveyors report on the Counter drain from Northey Gravels to Guyhirn giving details of cattle damage and noting that "the water level was only 18" below the land when readings were taken".

1762 - **4th District** Reported emergency pumping by horse mills without which the 4th District would have been laid near four feet under water.

1763 - **4th District** Reported area flooded by breaches in the bank of Smiths Leam. Other District, 2nd and 3rd, throw water upon the 4th so they cannot use the mills.

1746 - Ordered that new pointing doors with slackers be put into Cloughs Cross Sluice (the sluice was on the present New Wryde and discharged into the South Eau and thence along Straight Reach to Shire drain).

1767 - **North Level** - Henry Haynes supplied boats for carrying "Gault" to repair in the greatest emergency the North Bank - ordered that the Surveyor cut the weeds in the drains twice a year.

1768 - **North Level** Reported insufficient funds for the Maintenance of banks and drains.

1768 - **4th District** Proposed pointing doors in the Old Wryde to stop water going back instead of to the Sea.

1770 - Great Breach in the North Bank 130 yards long, 36 ft deep, the 2nd District under 7 to 8 feet of water.

1774 - **4th District** Mills to be put in good order and dressed with Tar and Oaker.

1775 - **4th District** New water wheel ordered for Parson Drove mill.

1777 - **North Level** ordered that Cloughs Cross sluice be rebuilt and enlarged and lowered further.

1778 - **4th District** Ordered a 20 ft wheel put into Murrow mill to replace 14 ft.

1783 - **4th District** Ordered that the following repairs be carried out to mills:
Murrow Mill - to put new ribs in her neck and dress her over with Tar.
Parson Drove Mill - to have three new sails, her cistern to be hitched, the wheels, new kings, the carcass to be repaired and two new boom parts.
Cant Mill - to have one new sail, a Cant beam, her gears fresh hung and dressed over with Tar
Neals Hundred Mill - to be dressed over with Tar and her fore waterways to be ripped and repaired.

1786 - **4th District** Ordered that the old axle tree from Neals Hundred Mill to be used to make a Waller for Murrow mill, present waller at Murrow mill used to make a new waller for Cants mill.

1787 - **North Level** Agreed that Thomas Grounds should establish a ferry across Smiths Leam at the Dog in a Doublet.

1790 - **North Level** Sum of £350 to be spent in scouring the Counter drain from the pointing doors at Knarr Lake to the Dog in a Doublet. Leave given to George Hemmant to lay a bridge over the Counter drain (Arnold Hemmant is a member of the present North Level).

1791 - **4th District** Ordered Parson Drove mill be repaired - "A new water wheel 18 ft dia., her ladles 18" wide with new shade over the water wheel, her carcass to be raised three feet and new boarded with whole Deal. To have a new spindle and two bray posts with a new axle tree, new top wheel with an entire new head, to have two new sails 36 ft long and the other two lengthened to the same dimensions with one new back, a new tailtree and two braces, her old spindle and one old back from Cants mill to be worked up for anchors.

1793 - **North Level** New bridge erected over Smith Leam at the Dog in a Doublet - built by public subscription.

1795 - **North Level** Major Flood in the Level caused by banks giving way, by slips 83,000 yards, by downfall 57,000 yards - Total 140,000 yards

1799 - **North Level** Major flood in the Level covered 35,000 acres.

LIST OF OCCURRENCES AND OTHER TRIVIA

1702	Anne Crowned
1704	Buckworth sluice erected
1700 - 1728	Duck Decoys constructed (first in Holland in 1678)
1714	George I
1720	Nat Kindersley's proposal to straighten and embank outfall to St Peter's Point
1724	Stephen Switzer invented plug drainage by hand
1727	George 2nd - 1728 Smiths Leam cut (Present River Nene)
1753	First North Level Act
1754	First Nene Navigation Act
1760	George 3rd - 1760 First pulled tenching plough to put in clay tiles 3 ft deep.
1763/4/7/70	Great breaches in the Nene bank - mole catchers appointed
1766	First Commercial Steam Engine
1769	Horse Mills still in use as portable pumps
1773	Kindersley's Cut completed
1771	Second North Level Act
1772	North Level 2nd District Act
1772	North Level 4th District Act
1775	Wisbech Northside Act
1782	James Watt Rotive Steam Engine
1784	Tax imposed on clay pipes, 5/- per 1,000, removed in 1826 providing they were stamped 'Drain'.
1786	Sugar Beet first planted
1790	First Optical Level/Theodolite
1794	Welland Bank Act - responsibility for maintenance taken over by North Level
1795	3rd North Level Act
1796	First Floating Steam Dredger
1796	Wisbech Canal opened

CHAPTER VII

Advancement in Technology

In 1783, George Maxwell was appointed agent to Lord Eardley Smith, who owned most of the First District, also land in the 5th District. Shortly afterwards he became Chairman of the First and was elected onto the Committee of the North Level.

John Wing, the Duke of Bedford's agent, became Treasurer of the North Level Commissioners in 1771 and was appointed a commissioner by the Duke for the Third District. He was a country banker and took the post without a salary: under the North Level Act, officials receiving a salary were not eligible to be Commissioners.

The appointed receivers for each District collected the acre tax in two parts: one for the upkeep of drains and engines in the District, the other to the North Level Commission for the upkeep of banks and main drains. This latter part was paid to the Treasurer who paid the North Level bills. The Receivers for the Second, Third and Fourth Districts were employed by John Wing!!

By 1788, George Maxwell understood the working of the North Level and discovered that far more was spent in the Second, Third and Fourth Districts than in the First and Fifth. At this time, the Duke of Bedford owned all the Third District, most of the Second District and some in the Fourth, and Commissioners, all the Duke's tenants, were appointed by him, obviously recommended by his agent.

The North Level Commission was made up of: First District, ten Commissioners, Second District seven, Third, thirty-four, Fourth, twelve, Fifth, fourteen. From these a committee of eighteen was elected: three from the First District, three from the Second, six from the Third, three from the Fourth and three from the Fifth District. Of these, at least ten were tenants of the Duke of Bedford which meant a majority controlled by John Wing, the Duke's Agent.

George Maxwell continued to request for work to be done in the First and Fifth Districts which were affected by over-topping of the Welland and Car Dyke banks, and he had discovered discrepancies in John Wing's accounting. Matters came to a head in 1789, when John Wing persuaded the Commission to promote an Act to raise taxes to cover arrears of payment and repay John Wing's expenditure. Maxwell, having discussed accounting procedures with the Chairman of the Bedford Corporation, confronted John Wing privately, threatening to publicly expose his dealings. Miraculously, the arrears of £800 disappeared as, according to the 1st District Minutes, did the amount owing to John Wing! George Maxwell toasted Wing at the lunch after the meeting at which the resolution requiring a fourth enactment was withdrawn, saying, "Oblivion to all animosities in the North Level". However, things did not improve; the drainage in the First and Fifth Districts was continually hampered by 'foreign water' entering these areas from the Car Dyke and the River Welland and George Maxwell continued to press for works.

In 1791, John Wing had bought a farm at Cross Guns from the Duke of Bedford. The North Level Committee approved considerable works on the North Barrier bank and Counter Drain, (remember the breaches in the seventies and the porous nature of the banks). Clay was imported from Whittlesey by boat and the banks were cored with puddled clay to prevent seepage. In July, 1808, it was recorded that George Maxwell complained about "monies being spent and works done in the Second District at the expense of the other Districts". He proceeded to list the urgent works required.

It had now become a personal battle between him and John Wing, which exploded on the 9th July at a meeting of the General Commissioners when the following resolution was passed, "that the thanks of the meeting be given to John Wing, Treasurer, for his great attention to the financial concerns, for his faithful discharge of his duties of the said office during the space of twenty-seven years without salary or remuneration and for his strenuous and unremitting exertions in maintaining the rights and promoting the interests of the said North Level and Porsand". It was further resolved that this should be printed in the Stamford and Cambridge papers and sent to the Registrar of the Bedford Corporation.

An interesting aspect is that the minutes were signed by John Wing, (Chairman), except where the minutes referred to him, when they were signed by Rev. Girdlestone, (Chairman). George Maxwell wrote to the papers pointing out that John Wing was in the chair as usual, not Rev. Girdlestone, he objected to the vote of thanks on the basis, "that no man who holds a place of profit can vote, as a Country Banker, holding balances in excess of £2,000 must receive considerable profits from interest". The Rev. Girdlestone replied, upholding John Wing, but George Maxwell persisted, although he was refused access to John Wing's accounts. However, on 3rd October, after Lord Eardley had contacted the Marquis of Exeter and other landowners, access to these was granted when Maxwell, Lord Eardley and Mr Wilnot, (Chairman of the Bedford Corporation), were in attendance.

They discovered that in the first year of John Wing's landownership in the Second District, £427 had been spent on bank repairs, when between 1780 and 1790, £485 had been spent on the First and Fifth Districts. Wing had paid £1,660 for the farm and after the bank repairs had been completed, had sold the farm for £7,000 "putting over £5,000 in his pocket - and this is the man who has been publicly thanked for his conduct".

By this time, Maxwell had ceased to be a North Level Commissioner and had become a member of the Board of the Bedford Corporation.

Further examination of the accounts showed that between 1800 and 1808, £11,960 had been spent on banks in the 2nd District and £2,522 on the Folly and Welland Banks. Maxwell stated publicly, "that there is no North Level Committee in which Mr Wing and the tenants of his Grace the Duke of Bedford do not hold a majority and pass situation and power to Mr Wing". He goes on to say that, "the men who also voted for the original resolution, (vote of thanks), were entrapped by the Arts of Sophistry" and he pledges to spare no expense to make an example of Mr Wing, calling on others to do the same. In June, 1809, John Wing resigned as Treasurer, but remained as a Commissioner, (he was still the Duke of Bedford's Agent). George Maxwell was proposed as the new Treasurer, but was outvoted and Thomas Steed Watson, (one of Wing's assistants), was appointed. In July of that year, Maxwell and Bevill were re-appointed Commissioners by Lord Eardley and Wing paid back £980 to the North Level, this figure being the discovered discrepancy in his accounts.

Maxwell persuaded the North Level Committee to commission Sir John Rennie to report on the state of the North Level banks. This report confirmed everything that Maxwell had been saying for the previous ten years about the First District and the Old South Eau.

Rennie's estimates of the works required were as follows:-

First and Fifth Districts: £18,950   Second and Fourth Districts: £11,200

He stated that the First and Fifth Districts were the worst drained and protected in the whole of the North Level areas.

The struggle for power in the North Level continued until 1817 when George Maxwell died, John Wing died shortly afterwards, in 1818. It is recorded that John Wing was a Commissioner for the Third District; his son, The Rev. John Wing, Commissioner for the Second District, the Rev. Girdlestone, Commissioner for the Fourth District, his son, Steed Girdlestone, Commissioner for the Fifth District and Tycho Wing, son of the Rev. John Wing, Commissioner for the Fifth District. The Treasurer, Thomas Steed Watson, was not a Commissioner as he was paid a salary of £40 per year. At Maxwell's death, there were three members of the Wing family and two of the Girdlestone family on the North Level Committee, with Tycho Wing elected as Chairman.

George Maxwell had battled for thirty-four years, although the Wing family still held the power. However, his efforts were worthwhile because, apart from the improvements being made in the First and Fifth Districts, the Wing family no longer held the purse strings. In addition, history shows that Tycho Wing, (who was by then the Duke of Bedford's Agent), was the right man for the Chair of the North Level and the Nene outfall Commissioners during his time. Although his grandfather appeared to be a rogue, there is no doubt that his grandsons' inherited knowledge of the North Level, handed down through three generations, was of immense value. Continuity of knowledge in drainage matters is as important today as then: "The Laws and Customs of Drainage are the most ancient in the Kingdom".

In the early Nineteenth Century, Tycho Wing records that in the North Level and Porsand Districts, there were 43 wind engines draining 48,000 acres, Wisbech Northside, Tydd, Leverington and Parson

Drove, 12 draining 17,700 acres, Sutton St Edmund two, draining 5,700 acres. Of these, 43 were large and seventeen small engines and the first steam engine was in Sutton St Edmunds.

The first commercial engine did not appear until 1776. The first engines used for pumping were single-cylinder, attached by a beam lever to a single-cylinder water pump, which lifted the water in a long stroke and spilled it out of the top, used initially in Cornwall's copper mines. Earlier, two large pumping stations were used to drain the Harlemmenmeer, Holland. The windmill came from Holland, but steam water-pumping came from England. The commercial engine utilised in England for pumping employed the same beam principle, but the fulcrum was toward the motive end, (single steam cylinder), and the end of the beam was attached by an arm to a huge flywheel on the shaft of the paddle or scoopwheel. The large stations had scoops instead of paddles and were up to 37ft in diameter.

In 1782, Watt invented the rotative engine, which drove a flywheel without need of a large beam. This engine became enormously popular in the early part of the nineteenth century for many practices as it could be made small enough to be portable, and the larger engines did not need huge stations to house them. However, this type of engine was slow to catch on in the fens, due to several factors. The massive heavy beam steam engines which required substantial piled foundation to carry the weight in the fens, were superseded by lighter engines supported on frameworks instead of solid structures.

Pumping accelerated the shrinkage rate of the silt and peat, requiring scoop wheels to be lowered; a costly and difficult operation. When lowering was required, this was often the spur to installing a larger wheel driven by the lightweight engine. A further development was a vertical paddle-wheel installed in a brick well, which forced the water outward, thus raising the level until it tippled out of the well at the top. The vertical spindle was driven by a toothed bevel wheel connected with bevel teeth on the flywheel, often made of Lignum Vitae. However, the major breakthrough, subsequently the saviour of the fens, was the invention, in 1851, of the centrifugal pump. The Appold pump, exhibited at the Great Exhibition, created a tremendous interest when it was realised that here was the means of pumping water against a head: no longer was it necessary to raise the pumped water above the downstream level. In spite of this, it was a complicated mechanical animal requiring water-proof seals and bearings: difficult and expensive to repair compared to the scoop-wheels. For this reason, its acceptance was slow in the fens where scoopwheels continued to operate until late in the century. This invention was the forerunner of the turbine pumps which followed in the Twentieth century. I would recommend reading, "Machines, Mills and Uncountly Costly Necessities" by Richard L Hills.

With the emergence of learned engineers, Drainage Commissioners became more aware of the hydraulic characteristics of channels in order to regulate flow. By 1800, all engines pumping into main channels had level gauges related by level to the sill of the controlling sluice for that drain. When the water reached a certain level in the receiving drain, pumping had to be stopped: this caused endless complaints that the Commissioners were not maintaining the drain or bank heights or, in the summer, cutting the weeds, also criticisms from the District Commissioner to the North Level Commissioners. Often there was insufficient wind in wet periods and land was saturated by seepage through banks. Although this appeared an argument for steam, the investment for a steam-powered engine was considerable, the running costs substantial compared to wind. The siltation of the Wisbech River and the various outfalls was affecting the ability of the main channels to cope with the now immense amount of water being pumped.

Technological advances in the nineteenth century were not confined to steam pumping; however, rapid development of the engine gave rise to portable engines, used for controlling water ingress during major channel excavations and sluice construction, and this process ceased to be a hand operation. Floating steam dredgers, land excavators, piling equipment, craneage, all became 'tools of the trade' for construction in land drainage, unfortunately resulting in a massive reduction in hand labour. Steel was taking over from cast iron, interlocking steel sheet piling as well as rolled steel joists were revolutionising construction, and by the end of the century reinforced concrete was being used. Automatic clockwork recorders for many applications became prevalent, automatic tide-gauges meant that a man with a watch and a level was no longer required, level recorders were installed in pumping stations and on main drains. Research into the hydraulic laws of flow in pipes was advanced, the understanding of laws related to the flow in channels and the effect of roughness was beginning to be more fully understood in upland channels where velocity was relatively high. It was not understood in Fenland channels and consequently most of the early major channel works were underdesigned, leading to successive failures. Communications and transport were improving rapidly; new fen roads were constructed and surfaced, making steam road transport more viable.

All in all, the technological developments of the nineteenth century were stupendous. However, the twentieth century was even more progressive in the land drainage field.

The problem with pumping engines, siltation and the ever present difficulty of land shrinkage, forced the Commissioners in the North Level to look into the possibilities of the long term answer. The latest techniques of producing levels indicating the available gradient of the surface of the water showed that there was a 5'6" fall from Borough Fen, (First District), to Gunthorpe Sluice, and a 13 foot fall at low water between the sill of the sluice to Crab Hole in the Wash. It should have been apparent that the solution was a new outfall channel to the Wisbech River, but nobody wanted to pay for it.

In 1814, James Rennie was invited by the North Level Commissioners to prepare a report and estimate of the necessary works. He found that the fall at low water between Wisbech Bridge and Gunthorpe Sluice was 4 inches and from there to Crab Hole: 13 feet. He proposed to cut a new channel through the lands from the end of Kindersley's Cut to Crab Hole as the sand of the wash would not support a new channel. He also proposed to improve the River Nene from Wisbech to Peterborough and internal channels.

The outfall channel would accept the waters from the North Level, South Holland and Wisbech Hundred. He suggested putting powerful steam engines to pump the water into the new channel at periods of high tides.

Several years of argument ensued between Wisbech Corporation, the North Level Commissioners and various Drainage Commissioners. Times were hard for the Fenmen: deterioration of drainage and successive wet years, increase in imports of cheap food, etc., had produced a depression in farming.

Tycho Wing took the Chair of the North Level in 1817, and from experience realised that the only step forward was the improvement of the Wisbech River outfall. He promoted this idea, producing his report in 1820, which was based on James Rennie's proposals of 1814, setting out how these works and the improvement to the North Level could be achieved. He noted that, "the upland floods come down more rapidly than in the past".

The North Level, Wisbech Corporation and several Drainage Commissioners were in conflict over the extent of the proposals and of course the costs. Wisbech Corporation appointed Thomas Telford to look after their interests, but not until 1828 did the interested parties agree to instruct Sir John Rennie and Thomas Telford to produce a combined report on necessary works. Tycho Wing's letters show how he laboured to promote this conclusion; Experienced and knowledgeable, his opinion was respected by these two eminent engineers.

In 1828, Pears, the North Level Superintendent, set out the route for a new channel and other works to the North level, which "would do away with Engines"!! Sir John Rennie agreed with his conclusions. The Rennie and Telford modified proposals were accepted by all parties, resulting in the Nene Outfall Act setting up the Nene Outfall Commissions, followed by the Second North Level Act in 1829, promoting the second major improvement to the North Level. The contract for the outfall cut from Gunthorpe Sluice to Skates Corner, thence to Crab Hole, was let to Messrs Toliffe and Banks on 2nd July, 1827, and was completed in June, 1830.

The route was through solid silt land, cut to a depth where the silt became saturated, with a dam at either end to prevent salt water ingress. A pilot cut was made and steam pumps for de-watering the excavation installed at the downstream end. The channel was then widened in steps, the material barrowed to form banks on either side. Some 1500 men were employed on the cut and 260 horses and for the work on the banks 900 men were imported from near and far, including Ireland, and housed in camps at Sutton Bridge. This caused difficulties for the locals: crowds used to gather outside the Bridge Hotel on Saturdays to watch the fights!

The two Engineers were confident that the channel would scour to the required depth without further excavation, after the success of a similar scheme on the Ouse Outfall, completed in 1821, although they were not sure of the speed or extent that this would happen upstream. The downstream dam was removed, three days later the upstream dam and the tide flowed into the new channel, although the old tidal channel was still open. After two weeks, it became clear that the expected scour was not taking place, so a dam utilising old barges and earth fill was hurriedly built across the old channel ensuring that tidal and freshwater flow totally directed into the new channel. These measures worked and scour in the new stone-lined channel, had become a deep-water channel to Wisbech by Spring 1891.

Associated with the new channel was the construction of a new bridge at Sutton Bridge and a causeway across the sands. The bridge was a Bascules Bridge like Tower Bridge, with two lifting spans of 26' and was erected before the new channel was opened, and the causeway after the dam was established, at the head of the New Cut.

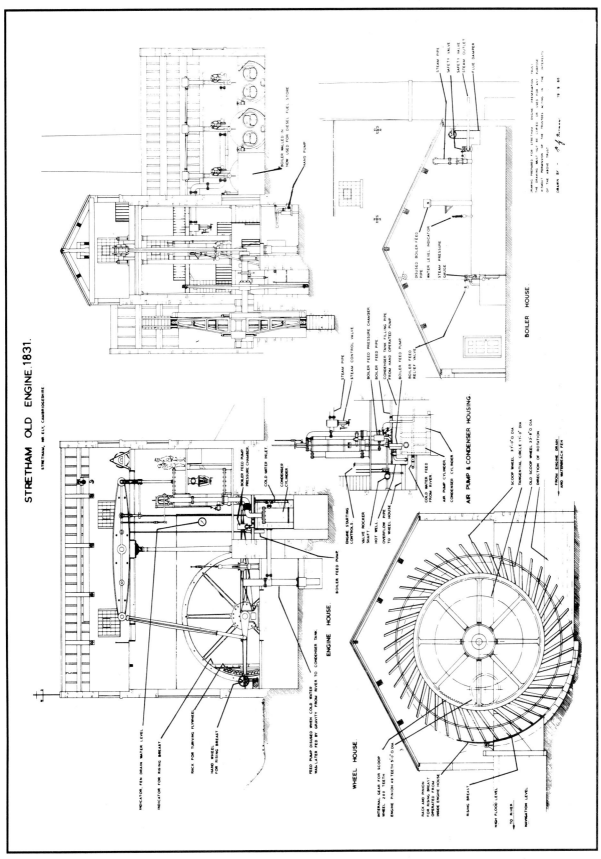

STRETHAM OLD ENGINE. 1831.

STRETHAM, NR ELY, CAMBRIDGESHIRE

Drawing of a Steam Scoop Wheel Engine

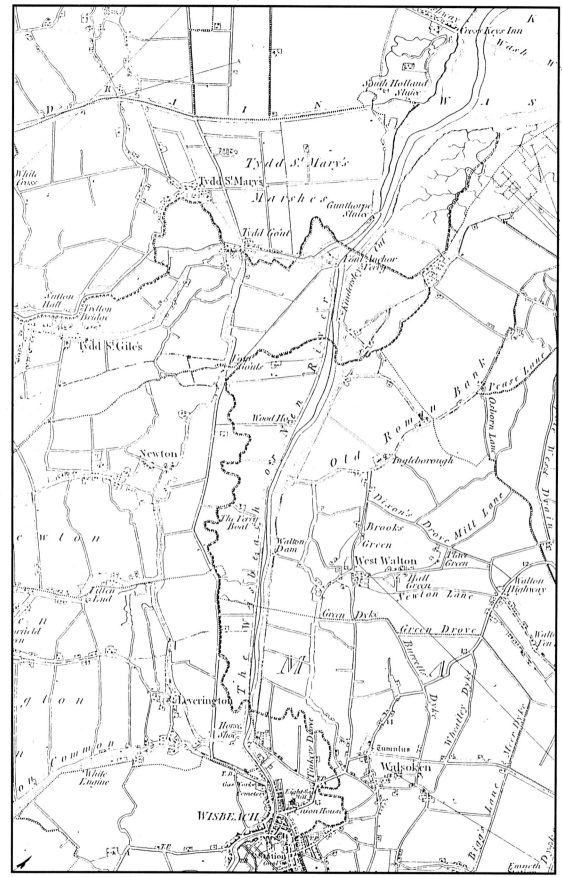

1" Ordnance Map of 1824

The bridge was used purely for traffic, forming part of the Swineshead - Fosdyke Turnpike Trust, pushing on toward King's Lynn. On 4th July, 1831, large crowds met the first stagecoach to use the bridge. This was the event which inaugurated a daily stagecoach service between King's Lynn and Newark - a journey taking just 15 hours. In 1850, the erosion of the channel bed and the excessive scour caused by the bridge created a difficult alignment for the shipping, and a new bridge was designed by George Parker Bidder, a partner with Robert Stevenson. The channel was re-aligned and the banks protected upstream and downstream. Resulting from work on London docks and elsewhere, Bidder was the first Engineer to understand the effect of tidal scour, but had not appreciated the problem of Fen silt.

It was a swing bridge used for road traffic only, until in 1864 the Midland Railway Act gave powers to use it for rail traffic. By 1895, this bridge ceased to be capable of carrying the new railway's loads and foundations were deteriorating. The present bridge was erected at a cost of £80,000, and tolls levied for crossing were at a penny ha'penny per head, a farthing per goose and ten pennies a score for sheep, which all proved highly unpopular. On one occasion, three young men swam the river and the fourth paid the toll and carried the clothes! The toll was withdrawn in 1903.

This same bridge has just been updated, modernised to hydraulic operation, replacing what were originally steam winches, subsequently motor winches, at a cost approaching £2 million. It is a listed monument!!

Sutton Bridge Dock was opened in May, 1881. The official opening, planned for the 29th June, never took place as part of the dock collapsed on the 9th, followed by collapse of the dock banks. It was never restored and is now a Golf Club, being purchased from the Sutton Bridge Dock Company in 1985. The consultants had no idea how to deal with the Fen silt!!

The reconstruction of Gunthorpe Sluice in 1773, after completion of Kinderley's Cut, created a new engineering strategy to keep the sluice from silting up. The channel from Hills Sluice, (Tydd Gote Bridge), to the new sluice was widened, deepened and the bank raised, Hills Sluice was made good and a reservoir formed between the two sluices. This enabled the tide to be let in during dry weather and released at low water, to scour out the outfall channel from Gunthorpe Sluice and keep the pointing doors clear of silt. The reservoir principle for flushing was created throughout the fens and subsequent to the construction of the new North Level Sea Sluice in 1829, a second sluice, the Protection Sluice, was constructed to form a reservoir and a pound for barge traffic.

We now know that by entraining a tidal channel, the rate of siltation can be reduced, but an element of consolidated silt remains which can only be removed by a major freshwater flood at low water. The Superintendents of Drainage Commissioners knew this, but apparently the eminent Engineers did not. Although the flushing principal of erosion was sound, it was still necessary to agitate consolidated silt during flushing for the best results.

At many of the older sluices in the Fens, including the North Level Outfall Sluice, are the remains of the old hand winches. They were sited either side of the outfall channel and were used to drag boards similar to the otter boards of a trawl, up, down, and across the channel as the trapped tide water was let out of the sluice.

Dealing with consolidated siltation of gravity outfall sluices has been a problem on the East Coast estuaries and tidal flat lands around the country for centuries and remains a problem today.

Tycho Wings Channel, as the new channel came to be known, was completed in 1830. The two lighthouses erected at the end of the channel were only used occasionally as such, and were actually follies to commemorate the works.

A short length of the existing channel upstream to Wisbech was straightened between 1827 and 1832 by the unemployed of Wisbech and known as Paupers Cut. The success of scouring of the bed which extended to Wisbech by 1832, can be judged by the tonnage registered in the Port:

1829	55,040 tons
1830	63,180 tons
1847	167,443 tons

At Wisbech before 1830, the tidal range was 4ft., by 1875 it was 15ft. and is now 21ft. The river bed in Wisbech had gone down by 10ft. This remarkable achievement had also reclaimed about 3,000 acres from the sea.

Drainage of the North Level and Great Portsand.

Preliminary Report and Estimate of the means of Improving the discharge of the North Level Waters from Clow's Cross to the Sea, addressed to the Committee of the Commissioners of the said North Level and Portsand.

GENTLEMEN,

In pursuance of an Order of the Commissioners of the North Level made at their General Meeting on the 7th July last and directing me, " to make a Survey and take the necessary levels between Clow's Cross and Kinderley's " Cut, for the purpose of ascertaining whether any and what improvement can be made " in the line of the Passage of the Waters from Clow's Cross to Sea, and at what " expence, and to report thereon to the Committee of the said Commissioners." I have directed my attention to the best means of carrying this highly important object into effect; and although the state of the harvest has not yet permitted me to take the required levels or make a detailed Survey, still understanding that it is in contemplation to take some immediate step in furtherance of the intended improvement, I beg leave to submit to you the following preliminary Report explaining my views of the best means by which that improvement may be obtained, and of the probable expence.

The Waters of the North Level and Portsand are conveyed by the drains for the respective Districts to Clow's Cross, where they all meet and pass by Shire Drain to Gunthorpe Sluice, and are discharged from thence into the estuary of Sutton Wash:

I propose that the present course of Shire Drain, which is extremely confined and crooked, and carried by a very circuitous route, and through such high lands that it could not be widened and deepened at any reasonable expence shall be abandoned, and that a new Drain shall be made extending in a straight line and north-easterly direction from Clow's Cross to the point where it crosses the road leading from Tyd Saint Giles to Newton, as shewn by the red line on the accompanying Plan, and from thence in a very gradual curve to the Turnpike Road leading from Wisbech to Tyd Gote a little south of the Tyd Gote Inn, from thence into the Old Shire Drain at the Red Gate and be discharged into Kinderley's Cut through a new Sluice a little north of Buckworth Sluice.

I propose that this Drain shall have a bottom thirty feet wide at its commencement at Clow's Cross, and gradually increasing to a forty feet bottom at the Outfall Sluice, the slopes to be one foot and a half horizontal to one foot perpendicular through the clayey soils, and three feet to one through the silt at the lower end, with an

2

inclination of four inches in a mile in the bottom of the Drain : the bed of the Drain at the lower extremity to be one foot below the cill of the Sluice, the forelands to be ten feet wide on each side, the earth to be laid in a proper form with a towing path on one side, in case it should be thought desirable to have the means of using the Drain as an occasional navigation. I am of opinion that the Soil along the proposed line of Drainage is principally Clay;—the land in general is low, and much of it of very inferior quality.

I propose also that the cill of the new Outfall Sluice shall be laid six feet lower than the cill of the present Gunthorpe Sluice,—I propose that this Sluice shall have two openings of fifteen feet each with pointing doors towards the Sea and draw doors to the Land,—I calculate that if this Drain and Sluice are made as I have recommended and the surface of the main river opposite the Sluice is lowered as much as may be reasonably expected by the opening of the new Channel now under execution from Kinderley's Cut to the Eye, the surface water in the Drain at Clow's Cross will not stand in times of heavy rain at more than six feet above the cill of the intended Sluice ; according to the best information I have at present been able to collect this will be sufficient for the general drainage of the Lands in the North Level, without the employment of the various engines now used; which as is well known answer their purpose for the most part very imperfectly.

The course of the proposed Drain is shorter by full three miles than the present course of Shire Drain, and in connection with this part of the subject I cannot help observing that still further relief might be obtained if the waters of the different districts in the North Level were conveyed to Clow's Cross by less circuitous routes than those which they now take: the new Drain would also afford the means of a perfect natural drainage to all the low lands in Wisbech Hundred lying on either side of it between Clow's Cross and Kinderley's Cut, as well as to those lands in Sutton Saint Edmund's and Sutton Saint James's, which now discharge their waters by Shire Drain.

I have added an Estimate formed upon such information as I have been hitherto able to obtain, but which of course will require a minute and careful revision after the Survey and Levels are completed.

I have the honor to be,

GENTLEMEN,

Your most obedient Servant,

Thomas Pear.

SPALDING,
5th SEPTEMBER 1828.

Thos Pear's report to the North Level Commissioners of 1828

ESTIMATE

Of the probable Expence of the proposed New Drain for discharging the North Level Waters from Clow's Cross to Kinderley's Cut.

To Eight Miles of New Drain Cutting	£24,000
To a new Sluice	7,000
To Bridges	3,000
To extra Work at Clow's Cross	1,000
To Land required for the Works	3,000
	38,000
To inlet communications for the Draining of Sutton Saint Edmunds and Sutton Saint James	2,000
	£40,000

Thomas Pears Estimate

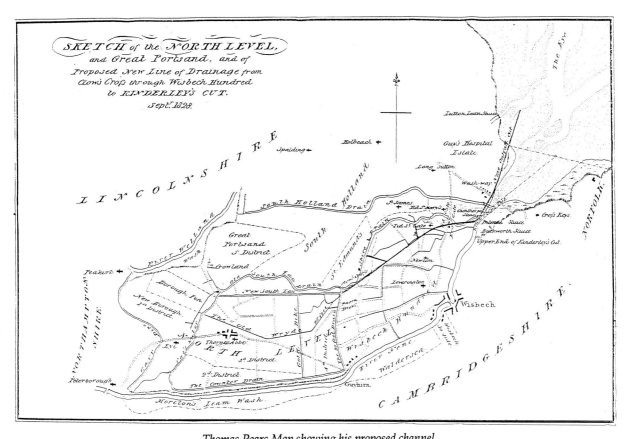

Thomas Pears Map showing his proposed channel

Typical Excavation of a Large Main Drain

Assessment of the flows to Gunthorpe Sluice and down the various main drains began in 1832. This was done by taking gauge readings at various structures at times when flooding occurred; these levels being the height of the river above the sill of the Outfall sluice, measuring the flow by means of floats timed over a fixed distance in the drains and the cross section of the structure, through which the water flowed. The gradient of the bed was ascertained by taking dips from a boat when there was no flow and the water surface gradient from the gauge reading differences during flow.

From these readings, the engineers of the day could work out roughly how much water came off the land for specific rainfall and what size of channel, with suitable gradient, would keep the water off the land in the low areas of the Level.

Work on the North Level Improvements began in 1829 with the construction of a new outfall sluice and subsequently the excavation of the new channel to Cloughs Cross. The invert level of the new sluice was 8ft. lower than Gunthorpe Sluice on Shire Drain. The new channel was cut deep enough to allow navigation to Cloughs Cross and, after completion of the works in 1834, Navigational Bye-laws were instituted by the North Level in 1836. Completion of the main drain, culminating in the new bridge and sluices at Cloughs Cross in 1834, enabled the North Level Commissioners to proceed with improvement of internal drains. The New South Eau was deepened and widened to the Old South Eau and a new cut formed to join up with Hundreds Drain to cater for the First District. The Wryde Drain was widened and deepened to Murrow and from there to Cloughs Cross to cater for the Third District.

The Catswater flow was reversed by improvement to a drain through Flag Fen to the Counter drain and the Counter drain improved eastward to Gold Dyke, Gold Dyke being improved Northwards to the Wryde, also to the South Eau, to cater for the Second District and Sutton St Edmund Little Common. The South Eau from Guyhirn to Cloughs Cross was improved to cater for the Fourth District.

It only remained to improve the channel across the Fifth District from Queens Bank to the Old South Eau at Dowesdale Bars, together with a new cut from there to the New South Eau, (Dowsdale arm), to complete the improvement required in the Act.

The Drainage Commissioners in the east of the Area were given the opportunity to reverse drainage water and take advantage of the new outfalls into the South Eau; Shire Drain from Denhams upstream became defunct. Wisbech Northside land was too low to take advantage so still required pumping.

Each of the Drainage Commissioners and the District Commissioners of the North Bank now had to embark on schemes to lower and improve their own drains, to take advantage of the lower levels, which took several years.

All this excavation had to be carried out by hand in the summer months, de-watering by buckets and manual lift pumps, a simple piston-type pump operated by hand over dams; two of these are in the North Level museum. Iron spades were used for hand digging, but wooden sloughs made of elm were used in soft, wet material, as this did not stick to them; heavy duty forks were employed to break up hard gravel and long-handled batter, (slope), knives used to shape bank slopes. Many of these slopes were turfed and faggots helped prevent erosion in the friable soils.

Tycho Wing summed up the success of the Second North Level Major Improvement Scheme by observing that, "in the winter 1836, we actually saw the water moving in the Wryde Drain at Thorney which no man had seen before".

The completion of these major works produced forty years of unparalleled prosperity in most of the North Level Area. There were still areas which were too low and therefore had still to be pumped: Newborough and Borough Fen in the First district, Flag Fen and the peat lands along the River Nene in the Second District and Wisbech Northside. The peat was still shrinking, but by 1875 most of the wind engines had disappeared.

A possible solution to the problem of dealing with these low areas without pumping was by 'warping', successful in the low areas around Goole in Yorkshire. A sluice with inward pointing doors was constructed in the tidal embankment and an area behind embanked, the area flooded on each tide and the doors shut as the ebb started. When the silt in suspension had dropped, the water was let out through small gates in the pointing doors. In three to four years, the deposited silt reached neap tide level enabling perfectly adequate gravity drainage to be achieved. In Yorkshire in the fifties, 'warping' was still being carried out. Warp is the Yorkshire term for silt. This was perfectly feasible in this region, as it was badly drained; the landowners were not prepared to give up income pleading that "they", (the Commissioners), "ought to do something about their drainage".

As the reclaimed silt marshes on the silt lands around the Nene estuary were at a level of ten feet plus, and the Black Land in the Second District at about one foot at that time, it puts the possibility of warping into perspective. Interestingly, there were no drainage authorities in Yorkshire similar in size or power to the North Level Commissioners!

The problems associated with the tidal sluices over the centuries kept occurring. In 1857, the new North Level Sea Sluice blew out on a high tide and the wing wall collapsed. Repairs were made, but it was decided to build a new sluice, which was constructed in 1859, designed by Stevenson and Bidder. This had longer cut-off piles, with puddled clay placed under the apron and between the headwalls. There was one set of pointing doors, two single swing doors and on the landward side, three penning sluices to hold water in the reservoir. The sluice was constructed on a new channel north of the old sluice pointing downstream instead of at right angles to the tidal channel. A fluted cast-iron footbridge was erected downstream of the doors and semi-circular cast-iron dam boards supplied to seat against the cast-iron columns to act as a tidal dam should work be required to the pointing doors or sills. This is the only bridge of its kind in East Anglia, probably in the country, and the usable cast-iron dam boards are still stored on site.

Tycho Wing's channel successfully increasing the depths at Wisbech, and the upsurge of the canal era, producing a network of water transport from the ports to the industrial north, prompted the Nene Valley Navigation Act in 1852. This Act provided for the improvement and deepening of the River Nene from the County Boundary at Wisbech to Northampton; the River Nene being fully canalised to connect with the Grand Union Canal.

Rennie, his son, Sir John Telford and Robert Stevenson, all considered that the restriction to flow on the River Nene were the 'S' bends through Wisbech from Phillips Brewery, (Elgoods), to Horseshoe Corner, and proposed a new channel bypass, but Rendel's report of 1849 concluded it was cheaper to improve the existing channel through Wisbech. The works first suggested were those between the Boundary at Wisbech and Peterborough.

The channel through Wisbech was deepened with limited widening and a new clear span bridge erected, excavation being carried out by steam dredger, and temporary dams erected at Waldersey and Guyhirn to give flotation to the dredger. In 1856, Mr Rendel, the engineer, died and his successor, Mr

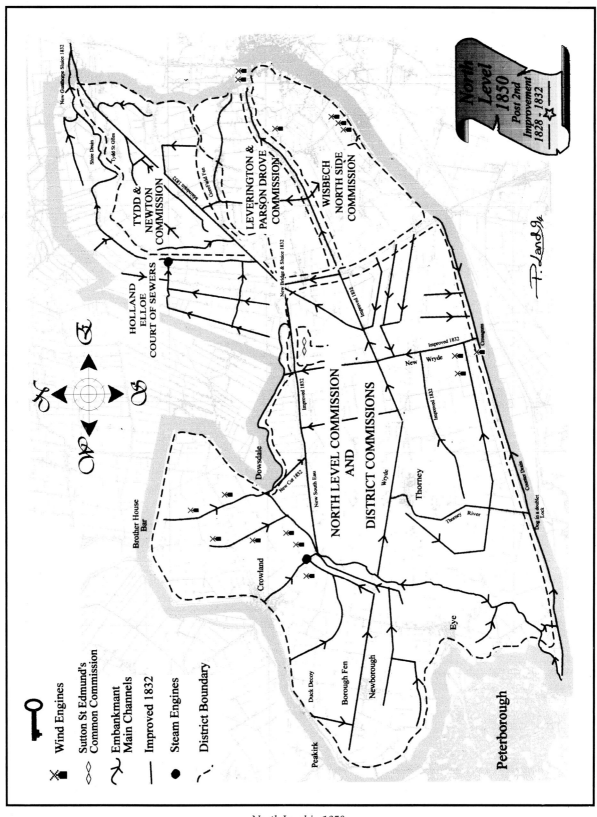

North Level in 1850

Fowler, was alerted to the slipping banks endangering the many warehouses. A dam, downstream of the bridge, costing £40,000, was proposed, but thrown out at Committee stage of the Bill to raise the money. Nothing was done and things got worse until, in 1857, Wisbech Corporation called in Stevenson and Bidder to report. Mr Fowler had, by this time, thrown a clay dam with gates either side across the river at Wisbech as a temporary measure to restrict flows. As a means of preserving the works already done and improving navigation and control of freshwater floods, Stevenson recommended the construction of a Tidal Staunch, with barge access, downstream of the bridge and stabilisation of the toe of the banks at a cost of £100,000 for limited works, and a new channel with sluice and lock as the complete answer for £250,000.

The improvement of the River Nene had, by 1858, reached the Dog in a Doublet and obviously Stevenson's recommendations for Wisbech had not been accepted apart from placing stone at the toe of the banks through the town. Fowler's temporary dam had either washed out or been removed, as had the dams at Waldersea and Guyhirn. The Second Navigation Act in 1862 dealt primarily with raising extra funds to deal with the excessive over-expenditure which had occurred.

By 1862, the channel had stabilized to a great extent and the predicted catastrophe for Wisbech did not occur; interestingly, however, the 1662 Act gave responsibility for the bed and banks of the River Nene from the Brewery to Horseshoe corner to the Burghers of the Borough of Wisbech.

The major flow in the Nene, resulting from the extremely wet year of 1875, produced further erosion in the tidal cut and flows through the North Level Sea Sluice created a huge scour hole downstream of the apron, causing undercutting and movement of the wing walls despite depositing quantities of stone in the bed off the end of the apron.

In 1875, Sir John Coode recommended a new sluice be constructed and the old sluice abandoned. Kingston, the Superintendent, had done excellent repairs to keep the sluice going, but by 1880 it was evident that major works were required urgently to prevent complete failure. Kingston reported to the Commissioners what should and could be done. Tycho Wing asked Sir John Coode to consider the proposals, he thoroughly approved, so work was started immediately and dams installed.

The old sluice was hurriedly opened at a high level with a limited opening to give emergency discharge, and the Protection Sluice, which had previously been opened, became the primary protection against tides. The extent of the damage was such that work needed took over a year to complete. The years 1875-79 were the wettest recorded since the major floods of the late eighteenth century and the difficulties with the outfall caused drainage problems in the level.

Sir John Coode, reporting in 1877, stated that land would have flooded even if the sluice had been fully operational. He recommended further lowering of the sills at Cloughs Cross and improvement to the new Wryde and Counter drain; the low land in the Second District along the Nene and Flag Fen were the areas flooding. Newborough and Borough Fen were now pumped with a steam engine.

These recommendations were immediately carried out, with only marginal success and these areas remained subject to flooding until, in 1880, a further report concluded that these areas were undrainable by gravity. They were peat areas and still shrinking. Coode suggested installation of two steam pumps at Cross Guns, but nothing was done by the North Level Commissioners.

1880 was the start of the great farming depression in the Fens, resulting from the very wet years 1875-79. With the advent of steam, much of the area was pumped, although most of the North Level drained by gravity, but still with a very high water table, the majority of the 97,000 acres being grassland. Steam engines, although effective, were costly to run; coal being very expensive to transport. The removal of the protection of the Corn Laws produced competition from overseas growers whose products were easily transported by steam-ships, and distributed to the now industrial north; the manufacturing revolution was in full swing and cheap food was required.

Some extracts taken from the Order Books and Minute Books of the various Drainage Commissions of the North Level during this century are listed below, although many of the books are missing.

EXTRACTS FROM THE MINUTES OF
THE COMMITTEE OF THE NORTH LEVEL COMMISSIONERS

The committee consisted of three Commissioners from each district and six from the Third District.

1805   Resolved to build new engine in Second District on Thorney Dyke.

1813   Navigation stopped on Shire Drain due to damage by bargees.

1814   Owners of Sutton St Edmund Little Common cut through South Eau Bank to let water off: warned that this was a "felony punishable by death without benefit of clergy".

1817 Tycho Wing in the chair

1825 Details of discussion on Rennie's report of 1814 when it was noted that "Floods came down more rapidly".

1828 Thos. Pears report on route of New Main Drain from Gunthorpe Sluice to Cloughs Cross.
Later that year, Telford and Rennie asked to survey the route and prepare a report for Parliamentary Bill.

1831 Money borrowed from Peckover and John Wing at 4½%. Land bought for £60/acre.

1833 Main Drain complete, ordered "to send a trustworthy man in a boat to collect materials scattered along the main drain and store them at Cloughs Cross". Ordered that New Wryde, Counter Drain and Catswater be roded three times a year. New set of "Rocking Shears" to be purchased, (used these on Counter Drain in1978, now in museum).

1834 Leverington and Parson Drove Commission allowed to drain into the main drain for £255 per annum.

1835 Northside (Part of) charged £100 per annum to drain into main drain, ditto for Tid and Newton Commission.

Letting:		
The Bedford Arms PH	The Dog in a Doublet PH	Fisheries
The Cross Guns PH	Guyhirn & Fengate Toll Houses & Tolls	Nene & Welland Banks - herbage
The White Swan PH		

Willow planted along Welland Bank at Crowland "to break up savage wash of the waves.

1836 Portable steam engine used for main drain sold. North Level Commissioners lease public house from Duke of Bedford purchased in 1911, at this time, men paid partly in "beer dockets".

1843 Officers ordered to arrange for roding to be carried out by the "piece" (piecework).

1847 Report on success of Tycho Wing's Chanel.

Tonnage handled in port	1929 - 55,040	1830 - 63,180	1847 - 167,443

1830 Tide rise in Wisbech was 4ft, is now 15ft.

1848 Agreed for John Graveside to take earth from above ground level on the Main Drain for "making draining pipes and other draining articles".

1854 Tolls still being collected at Guyhirn.

1857 North Level Act to allow for construction of New Outfall sluice, (original "blew out"), and improvement works.   Report on Drainage of North Level by Borthwick and Stevenson to decide whether pumping was necessary.   Thorney water supply constructed.

1858 Reconstruction of the Dog in a Doublet Bridge and a new lock for the Thorney River under Nene Improvement and Navigation Act.

1859 New Outfall Sluice completed two feet lower. Main Drain lowered to Tydd Gote Bridge.

1861 Clowes Cross Sluice invert lowered 5'. Main Drain improved - New Wryde. Ordered locomotive weight limit notices on bridges. (Same notice erected at Cloughs Cross in 1978!)

1862 Works recommended by Stevenson to save pumping completed. Commented that eventually may need to pump at Cross Guns.

1865 Reported tide leakage under the New Sluice. Bidder to supervise repairs, (Engineers still did not understand how to stop flow through Fen silt).

1868 Outfall sluice still leaking. Agreed to erect protection sluice inside piled cofferdam which would become part of permanent works - designed by Stockman C.E. (First time long cut-off piles used to prevent flow through silt).

1869 Reported stock crossing the river at Cross Guns. Steam dredge purchased. New lock gates and Penn Sluice in Thorney River constructed.

1870 Thos. White appointed assistant superintendent to Kingston. Required to keep a horse and paid 40/- a week including horse. Bank of main drain raised above high tide level between outfall and protection sluice. Boat house built at Clowes Cross for dredger and two barges.

1874 Sir John Coode asked to report on leaking outfall sluice. Recommended abandoning same and build new one - nothing done.

1877 Sir John Coode report on the drainage of the North Level. Further lowering of Cloughs Cross. The North Level Commissioners' annual inspection including the outfall took three days by coach and horses.
Bill of fare for one lunch as follows:-

Salmon   Soles
Cucumber and Lobster Sauce

_____

Fish   Meat   Fowl

_____

Pudding   Cheese   Dessert

_____

Roast Beef   Roast Lamb   Roast Veal
Boiled leg of Mutton   New Potatoes

_____

Ducklings   Roast Chickens   Boiled Chickens
Oxtongue   Green Peas   Cauliflower

Jellies   Gooseberry Tart   Cheese Cakes
Custard

Cheese and Salad

Desserts

1881   North Level Outfall Act passed to include Coode's recommendations excluding pumping. £5,000 borrowed from Peckover at 4%.

1883   Repairs to outfall sluice complete. Ordered old sluice banked up and arches filled with soil.

1884   Ordered that Hannath's Bridge be removed and re-erected at Black Dyke as a "horse bridge" - still there.

1889   Committee refused to cut weed or clean out Counter Drain downstream of sewage works, (1992 - sewage still flows down the Counter Drain to the Dog in a Doublet).

1892   Fred Ashworth appointed superintendent of works to the Commissioners at £3 per week including a horse.

1896   Reported leakage through the doors at the Outfall Sluice. Ordered a diving survey - repairs carried out. The following twenty years were very uninformative, obviously because no money was available due to depression. Opposition raised to many bills, usually withdrawn when saving clauses for North Level Commissioners were inserted.

FIRST DISTRICT, BOROUGH FEN AND NEWBOROUGH MINUTES

1809   Reference to mills lately built, (one built probably in about 1760 followed by a record to raise water higher, both situated at Hirne, now known as "The Engine", Crowland).

1810   Ordered that a new Great Mill be erected at the South Eau.

1812   Act of Draining, Enclosing and Improving - Borough Fen Common and the Four Hundred acre common and forming same into a parish to be called Newborough of about 6,000 acres in the First District of the North Level. (These areas were exempt from the taxes of the Great Level).
The new Commissioners were made responsible for the Car Dyke and Folly River to the Welland. Common Wasteland to be sold to defray the costs of improvements. Four Hundred Acre Common to be in Parish of Crowland and not Newborough.

1814   Highland Drain and Hundred Drain improved 20' bottom and 1:1 side slopes.Drain improved from Folly River to the Welland and banks raised. Required to set out roads in the parish.

1816   Maxwell resigned. Old ship sails purchased for large engine. New sails for Buck Mill by Thos. Pear. Agreed to pay 2/- per day for working mills at night.

1820   Contracted with Thos. Pear to erect 70 H.P. steam engine. Ordered that banks of the Car Dyke and Folly River be puddled. Steam engine completed.

1821   Enclosure completed and all common land sold.

1822   First meeting of the Newborough Drainage Commissioners under 1819 Act. Ordered that safety rails be erected at steam engine.

1824   £1. 9s. 0d. spent on sail cloths for Red Engine, Lot Engine and Low Fen Engine.

1829   Request to lower Lot Engine, (major improvement to North Level pending). Reported that steam engine cost £330. 7s. 5d. per year whilst Brick Mill cost £21.19s. 0d. (This was the reason why steam engines were slow to be adopted). Ordered one hundred chaldron of Elsicar Hard Coal.

1833   New Cut from the engine to the New South Eau made. Ordered that brick mill be removed.

1834   Hundred Drain lowered and widened, costs shared with First District, and cut extended to Hundreds Drain from the engine.

1837   Resolved to sell steam engine.

1839   Resolved to put in new tunnel at Peakirk Bridge to let in freshwater after complaints from Deeping Fen that too much water was being taken from the Welland. Welland outlet stopped off after lawsuit.

1880   Ordered that the tunnel under the Folly, (which drained Peakirk), was to be closed as it was solely for supply of   freshwater to the District.

1881   Inspection carried of tunnel under the Folly

1883   The Court Action regarding flooding of Peakirk land resulted in claims of £3,180 and costs being awarded against the Commissioner. New Act to raise funds to pay for compensation and works to the Folly River.

1899   Newborough still rated by the acre, irrespective of productivity.
Williams, surveyor, died after 40 years service.

SECOND DISTRICT MINUTES

Minute and order books missing between 1754 and 1913.

THIRD DISTRICT MINUTES
Minute Books Missing

FOURTH DISTRICT MINUTES

1801 John Hemmant, owner of 500 acres, declared himself his own commissioner. Resolved that new mill be erected with new mill drain. Several mill drains given up and new ones taken over.

1802 Mention of Neptune Mill, (obviously the new one).

1803 Reported that the new mill was in "a very imperfect and insecure state."

1805 Ordered that landowners clean their dykes of reeds within 14 days. Ancient Statute.

1807 Sutton St Edmund Common requested to drain their land through the 4th District - refused - (typical parochial attitude).

1815 New sails and break wheel for Neals Hundred Mill, new break wheel for New Mill and a new sail for Murrow Mill.

1818 John Burdeck estimated dyking work required the persons benefiting to advance the money, to be repaid out of rates, (they were not able to carry balances to tide them over until the rates came in. Dyking was carried out and paid for by owners who were repaid over two years).John Oldfield to immediately repair Parson Drove Mill, a new water-wheel and new trough. Diameter of wheel to be increased by two feet.

1819 Ordered that a new pair of pointing doors be put down near Cloughs Cross on the 30' (New Wryde) to prevent water being taken out of the drain by Sutton St Edmund Common.

1825 John Steed Girdlestone, younger, appointed Collector and Treasurer, John Wing of Wisbech appointed Clerk and Solicitor!!

1826 New bridge built in the great road across Parson Drove Mill drain (this is an interesting specification): "The waterway 10' wide, carriageway 14' wide, walled a sufficient height for the carriageway, wings 4' long exclusive of pier, walls, springing walls and buttresses 2 bricks thick, wings 1.1/2 bricks thick, railed with oak 6" x 4" two rails high. The brickwork of the walls to be covered by 3" thick planking tied down at each end with iron ties.
FOUNDATIONS - Mud sills - planked under springing walls and buttresses according to the plan - to be done with cinder and mortar and to be grouted every second course or third course. the whole of the work to be executed with good new materials and the contractor to have expense £58 and no charge to be made for any extras. The work to be completed in one month under penalty of £20." (A bit different from today's contract conditions).

1828 Thos. Pears of Spalding asked to advise "as to what alterations it is advisable to make to the water wheel and other works of the new mill to enable her to go in light wind". Reported that the new mill "cannot get rid of the water as quick as necessary.

1829 Agreed to draining Sutton St Edmund Common to Parson Drove Mill as a temporary measure as the mill for draining this area becoming useless. Dead-headings, (dams), to be put in to prevent "Communication" with this area.

1833 New tunnel made into the New Wryde, (after the North Level Commissioners' improvements) from Bishoplands. Compensation to be paid by Sutton St Edmund Common for use of the 4th District's Mill. North Level asked to carry out further works for the 4th District affected by water from the New Wryde - drains being improved.
Note:- The Fourth District was now taking advantage of the North Level's new channel to the sea from Cloughs Cross.

1836 Resolved that men employed on roading the drains supply tools at their own expense and repair same so no expense falls on the Commissioners.

1849 Further lowering of tunnels into the North Level main drains. Owners told to remove tunnels or renew to a larger size and lower level.

1854 The Committee consider the great obstruction to the drainage between Cloughs Cross and The Sea Sluice. The Committee are of the opinion that it is impossible for the Fourth District to be drained without the use of steam power.

1860 Mole-catcher appointed.

1881 Rate of 2d per acre laid.

1897 Gauges to be erected at outfalls to the North Level drains.
The success of the North Level major improvement can be judged by the fact that the 4th District did not require to carry out any major improvements between 1861 and 1900.

FIFTH DISTRICT MINUTES
Minute Books Missing

WISBECH NORTHSIDE COMMISSIONERS' MINUTES

1775 Drainage Act - The minutes have disappeared from this date to 1914 - the following is from the Hundreds of Wisbech Commissioners of Sewers.

1885 Court agree to replace brick outfall outlet with iron tunnel at Rummers Mill - outfall to the new steam pumping station with Appold centrifugal pump.

1897 Approved application to let in freshwater from the Wisbech River - the top two feet were considered fresh.

TYDD AND NEWTON DRAINAGE COMMISSIONERS' MINUTES

1803 Drainage Act adding 100 acres Farm and Tydd St Mary Fenn. Prior to 1878 pages have been torn out of Minute book, no doubt for some ulterior motive.

1892 A Mr Smith had erected tunnel through Roman Bank allowing water to flow into the District.

1897 Complaint to North Level Commissioner allowing high water to flow into the District. North Level agreed to operate sluices to allow low land to drain.

LEVERINGTON PARSON DROVE DRAINAGE COMMISSION'S MINUTES

1801 Drainage Act.

Minutes are missing from 1801 to 1891

By this time, the "Little Cut" from Bores Gote to the Eau was in existence, probably cut in 1834. Gorefield Fen was still outside the area of the Commissioners. It is recorded that owners in the Fen should pay £10 per year to drain into the "Little Cut".

ADMINISTRATION FROM THE 1770's

The administration of the North Level Commissioners' area, with its five internal districts was well established. The remaining part of the present North Level area was still administered by the Hundreds of Wisbech Court of Sewers operating under the restrictions of the 1531 Act and only able to raise funds for the MAINTENANCE of sewers and banks.

With the deterioration of the outfalls into the Nene estuary, landowners became aware of the need for improvements. This, together with an element of parochiality, prompted areas to seek their own identity and hold their own purse strings. The Tid and Newton Act of 1773 set out their area of responsibility, their powers of laying rates to recover the cost of maintenance and improvements: they were empowered to raise loans to contribute to the proposed new outfall channel. This was followed by the Wisbech Northside Act in 1774 with similar powers and in 1801 by the Leverington and Parson Drove Act.

The Drainage commissions, although limited to the tax per acre they could levy, were nevertheless given powers to raise loans for a maximum figure under the act. They employed clerks and superintendents to supervise the collection of rates and works of maintenance and improvements. However, the Commissioners were not generous employers.

The Sutton St Edmund Little Common became independent in 1808, the 2nd Northside Act followed, which raised the borrowing and rating limit, as did the Tydd and Newton Act of 1807.

Within the North Level, Acts related to improvements followed thick and fast, with the Newborough Act in 1812 and 1819, the Nene Outfall, 1827, allowing Tycho Wing's Channel, followed in 1829 by a request for more money. Again, in 1836, the North Level required more money for the Nene outfall and North Level.

The Bedford Corporation, with little influence over the North Level since the early part of the century, was finally wound up under the Dissolution of the Bedford Corporation Act in 1857.

The General Drainage Act of 1861 created Drainage Boards of elected members with powers of borrowing and differential rating tied to valuation. They were set up by the Enclosure Commissioners, (later the Ministry of Agriculture and Fisheries), when petitioned by proprietors of not less than 10% of the land in the drainage area and supported by owners of two thirds of the land.

By 1927, 200 of the then 361 Drainage Authorities had been brought into being by special Acts of Parliament. including all the authorities in the North Level.

Proprietors of 20 acres of land qualified as Commissioners for the Drainage Commission ; an owner of 100 acres could be appointed a deputy commissioner, over 200 acres entitled two deputies.

In the North Level, the districts appointed their commissioners who then formed a working committee of eighteen. The Commissions in the North Level operated satisfactorily within their legal constraints, but the main river flowing through the Level was a different matter.

Successive Acts related to the River Nene meant responsibilities were again controlled by Commissioners, so by the 1860's there were numerous commissions each with different responsibilities, all the Commissioners being appointed by the Drainage Commissions contributing to the cost of improvement. The Nene Outfall Commissioners were accountable for the channel and banks between the lighthouses and Horseshoe Corner, except for banks constructed before the Act, which were supervised by the Drainage Commissioners alongside the river. Banks and Channel from Horseshoe Corner to the brewery were looked after by Wisbech Corporation.

The bank of the river between the brewery and Guyhirn was the charge of Northside and Waldersea Commissions, the bed and wash being in the hands of Nene Improvement Commissioners under the 1851 Act. The North Bank of the Nene between Guyhirn and Peterborough was owned and controlled by the North Level Commission, but the bed, an area between the river and the newly erected cradge bank on the Nene washes, was looked after by the Nene Improvement Commissioners.

For example, Tycho Wing was, at one time, the Duke of Bedford's agent for the Thorney Estates, the chairman of the North Level Commissioners, chairman of the Nene Outfall Commission and chairman of Newborough, the 1st and 3rd District Commissioners of North Level - all that commitment and attendance without attendance expenses!!

The accounts of the North Level, its Districts and the Nene Outfall Commission, were administered by the North Level, rates raised by them and credited to different accounts. Small wonder sensible men suggested Conservation Boards for main rivers from the source to the sea. Bills presented to Parliament in 1877, 1878, 1879 and 1881, were all thrown out due to objections from the Uplands at being rated for works from which they received no benefit. This state of affairs continued until the formation of the Catchment Boards under the 1930 Act.

Essex Street Works, Strand, London, W.C.   **43**

GWYNNE & CO.'S IMPROVED WIND POWER PATENT PUMPING MACHINERY,

Adapted to the requirements of the Colonies (for Drainage, Irrigation, etc., etc.) and open situations, where steam or water power machinery cannot be applied.

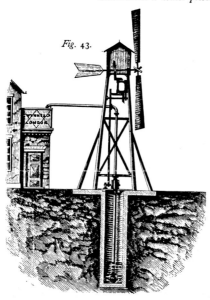

Fig. 43.

FIG. 43. The Wind Power Pumping Machinery is simple, will work continuously day and night when the wind blows, is not likely to get out of repair, and requires but little attention. GWYNNE & Co.'s Improved Centrifugal Pump possesses the great advantage of discharging a quantity of water equal to the square of the velocity, thus *double the velocity* will raise *four times the quantity* of water to a given height, or it will raise the same quantity *to four times the height.* It will thus be seen that this pump acts as a safety governor to the Wind Engine, and when the wind blows very strong, the immense quantity of water raised prevents the Wind Engine from running too fast, and at the same time *usefully applies the power, which would be entirely lost with any other description of pump.* Where steam power or a Turbine can be used it is preferable to wind power, which is uncertain, as there is often no wind when pumping is most required. The engraving shows the pump as applied to raising water into a tank. This arrangement has also been applied to the supply of Railway Stations with water, for raising water for cattle, &c., &c.

PRICES.

Wind Engine, 17 feet diameter, Four Sails, with Driving Gear, and No. 1 C Centrifugal Pump, with 30 feet Pipes and Valve, will raise about 20 gallons per minute **£86**

Wind Engine, 25 feet diameter, Four Sails, with Driving Gear, and No. 3 C Pump, with 30 feet Pipes and Valves, will raise about 80 gallons per minute **£130**

Wind Engine, 30 feet diameter, with Gear and Pump, and 30 feet Pipes and Valve, will raise about 120 gallons per minute **£250**

Wind Engine, 50 feet diameter, with Gearing and Pump, and 30 feet Pipes and Valve, will raise about 500 gallons per minute **£300**

Wind Engine, 70 feet Sails, with Gearing and Pump, and 30 feet Pipes, will raise about 2,000 to 3,000 gallons per minute **£800**

Larger Pump for low lifts.

Prices for other sizes may be had on application.

The poles or woodwork are not included in the price, being obtainable usually on the spot.
The height the water is thrown is calculated at 20 to 25 feet, but the machinery can readily be adapted for elevating it to any other height that may be desired. Brick or masonry towers are more permanent structures than wood, and in many situations have been adopted. GWYNNE & Co.'s Pumping machinery can be adapted to Windmills at present in existence.

Gwynnes Wind Pump of 1869

CHAPTER VIII

'In Living Memory' - The Twentieth Century
Changing Patterns 1900-1930

The closing years of this century are an ideal time to record developments in drainage, engineering and administration throughout.

The nineteenth century Industrial Revolution made Britain prosperous, and shifted power from land ownership to industrial wealth. The thirst for individual wealth became insatiable, the streets of the centres of industry and commerce seemed paved with gold.

People began to leave agriculture, cheap food was imported, industrial development and urban sprawl decimated the environment. With money being poured into industry, housing and transportation, little was available for agriculture, so the century began with a slump in farming.

However, the depression in farming affected the North Level differently from the Uplands. The silt and clay lands could produce not only cereals, but vegetables and fruit; the land's ability to grow potatoes and sugar beet accelerated the use of these crops, and by 1903, the last rape-oil mill in the area at Wisbech closed down. Woad was still grown on the smaller farms around Wisbech, but by 1921, this crop had died out, the last woad mill at Parson Drove closing in 1914.

Small steam tractors, the Ivel manufactured by Albone of Biggleswade, appeared in 1902 and were in production until 1921. However, the Americans began developing the Gas Traction Engine, manufactured by the Gas Traction Company of Minneapolis in 1904, the first experimental Ford tractor in 1907, and production of Gas Tractors by Sowyer-Massey in 1910. By the start of the 1914/18 war, the farm tractor was seen on the larger Fen farms. Although only suitable for load-bearing soils, their progressive use marked the decline of that stalwart, the heavy horse.

Throughout 1912, the North Level suffered; heavy rainfall culminating from 20th to 26th August in a downfall amounting to 4.09 inches. The yearly rainfall average between 1893 and 1912 was 19.88 inches, but in 1912, 28.51 inches were recorded. Problems were compounded in August when floodwater from the Welland at Peakirk entered the Newborough and First District, flooding that area and increasing the considerable load on the New South Eau. Much of the North Level region was flooded or water-logged and the "new fangled" tractor was useless. Cereal crops were lost and the potato crop failed.

All North Level Districts and the contributory Boards petitioned the North Level Commissioners to investigate. Sir John Coode, who in 1880 had recommended pumping at Cross Guns to relieve the gravity system, produced his report in 1913 commenting that, "they were of the opinion that no reasonable pumping plant which could be erected and no reasonable extension and enlargement of outfalls, main drains or other drains which could be made, would have prevented the serious flooding in Autumn last year. Any works or machinery to prevent flooding with such rainfall as that of the week Twentieth-26th August are out of the question". He estimated that discharge at the outfall sluice by gravity averaged $1/8$th inch of rain per day over the whole North Level Area.

Sir John Coode appears to be the first engineer to take account of the state of saturation of the ground, (soil-moisture deficit - in modern terms), pointing out that after two days during the fatal week the ground became saturated and further rain ran off immediately. The North Level Superintendent had observed this effect and taken gaugings on the Main Drains.

At this time, much of the North Level was in transition from grass to arable, but the drainage regime was still designed to retain high water levels for cattle-fencing and a high water-table for the grass. Throughout the area, adjacent farms were either still grass or had become arable, often privately pumped, which produced a myriad of dams, "slackers" and sluices which were only removed or opened when flooding became apparent. At this period, all water had to be discharged by gravity at Tydd, 17 miles from Peakirk in the First District, an impossible situation. Coode recommended installing a small pumping station at Cross Guns for £10,000, improvements to the Folly River Bank, restoration of Peakirk Bridge Pointing doors and removal of the sewage discharge from Peterborough to the Counter Drain.

The state of country estates was highlighted by the Duke of Bedford's report in 1897 on the involvement of the Russel family in Fen drainage and the creation of the model township of Thorney. He wrote: "In the period 1816-1897 taxation of the Thorney Estate was £614,714. The Bedfords expended £983,640 on soils which was reclaimed by his ancestor for £100,000. Eighty years' taxes amounted to $^9/_{10}$ths of the net income. In 1895 some £8,568 was paid in general taxation leaving a deficit of £441 on the year's working, a return on capital estimated at $2.^1/_7$th%.

"My ancestor's vision of a beautiful mansion surrounded by every conceivable luxury did not exist. The only pleasure which I and my forefathers have derived from Thorney is the kindly feeling which existed between us and our tenants and the inhabitants of Thorney Town. It was no doubt a pleasure to my predecessors to evolve a pretty village out of the dreary waste of the Fens, to create a charming river with well-wooded banks and to make life less malarious (Ague) and less miserable by a complete fresh water system and sewage system....

"They have their reward in the excellence of health in Thorney, in the practical disappearance of crime and the extinction of pauperism, but the economic critic is right in his report that such results do not show pecuniary profit".

The depressed state of agriculture and the financial difficulties of large landowners finally led to the demise of the Duke's estate in Thorney after some 360 years when, in 1910, it was split up, and sold, most farms being purchased by sitting tenants like the Hemmants, Smiths and Gees.

The Act of 1912 created Thorney Drainage Board with unique powers and responsibilities, being made responsible for all the functions carried out by the Duke of Bedford in Thorney and the surrounding farmsteads. They were accountable for the drainage of the old 3rd District of the North Level, also for the following activities:

(1)   Supply of freshwater to the village via the Thorney River.
(2)   Sewage disposal and night soil collection.
(3)   Roads.
(4)   Fire Service and provision of engine.
(5)   Street lights.
(6)   Saw mill
(7)   Distribution of freshwater to the outlying farms from the Thorney River and main drains.
(8)   Dog in a Doublet public house.

Road, lights and night soil collection were passed to the RDC and CC in 1915. Fire service and engine were taken over by the Parish Council in 1919, and the saw mill was sold in 1932, but piped sewage disposal, (grass treatment), and water supply were not taken over by the RDC until 18th July, 1933, along with the building and steam pumps, for £200.

However, when the Duke of Bedford created Thorney Town, a permanent injunction was approved by Parliament to prevent the hard gravel shoals being removed from the River Nene at the Dog in a Doublet and Northey, as at that time they created the salt water limit on the river except for major tides or surges. Water was extracted from the river through the lock at the Dog in a Doublet into the Thorney river to Thorney, thence into the old Wryde drain. Water was distributed along the main drains to the farmsteads for drinking water, both cattle and human! In the rest of the North Level area the contributory Boards' domestic water was procured from so called Freshwater Sumps.

Transition from grassland to arable farming caused even more difficulties in the Thorney Drainage Board area, due to this legal undertaking to supply water which necessitated excessive maintenance to the drains involving weed cutting twice or three times a year, desilting the drain bottoms and clearing out "the enemy of Fen drainage" known as Cott, a floating algae which looks like green cotton wool. This supply requirement caused the Board problems in the wet year, 1912.

The 1913 Coode report was accepted by the North Level Commissioners, but doubtless due to the agricultural financial situation, was only partly acted upon. The Folly River was put in order by the First District, and Newborough, financially assisted by the North Level, and Peterborough Council installed a steam engine to pump treated sewage into the River Nene in times of high water in the Counter Drain.

Possibly relieving some flooding in the 2nd and 4th Districts, difficulties of water quality extracted from the River Nene could arise. Piped water supply did not reach Thorney until 1952! The 1914 war signalled the end of the farming depression: more food was needed, prices recovered as overseas' cheap foodstuffs became unavailable. Grants were more attainable to break up grassland and maintain essential main drains. Steam pumps were erected by the Second District in 1914, Thorney Drainage Board in 1915, plus several private pumps, all discharging into the New Wryde.

So important was the agricultural war effort, that 6,000 Fordson tractors were imported in 1915, rotary under-drain machines were supplied by the government and grants obtainable for under-draining newly broken up grassland. The North Level 1st and Newborough and the 5th, (Great Porsand), were the most difficult areas to drain, particularly the areas of Fen which had probably wasted by at least 18 inches in the previous century.

Although these areas had been pumped by wind engines and subsequently steam, in Newborough, these drainage machines were removed when the main drain was cut and the New South Eau improved, Great Porsand benefiting further by the Dowsdale Arm connection to the main drain. These areas were aided by the improvement of internal drains to take advantage of the "great new works" after 1832, but with the peat shrinkage and change in agricultural patterns, the long gravity drainage system was, by 1900, unable to cope with the modern drainage standard required.

Unfortunately, the minute books of the 5th District, until 1942, are missing, so little information is available. However, we know that the transition from grass to arable was much slower in this district than in the rest of the the North Level.

After all, the North Level Commissioners were responsible only for the main channels taking drainage water to the sea at Tydd and for embankments alongside the rivers Welland and Nene, all the internal drainage being the responsibility of the District Boards.

The standard of maintenance and improvements of drains depended on the "ability to pay" which depended on the size of the farm holdings and productivity; the latter dependent on drainage, compared with other Districts, the 1st and 5th Districts were poor relations in many ways, especially in relation to protection embankments.

In the 1st District, before the cutting of the Folly River in 1712, all the upland water from Peterborough and Marholm, (The Maxey area, was discharged along Highland Drain, (Vermuyden Peakirk Drain). When the upland water was cut off, Newborough was able to cut a new Highland Drain northwards to the New South Eau.

However, the Newborough Commissioners retained the responsibility for the Car Dyke and Folly River channel and banks to the Welland, a considerable financial burden. The Newborough Drainage Commissioners were formed resulting from the partition of Borough Fen Common and shouldered responsibility for all culverts, bridges and road constructed by the Borough Fen Partition Board as well as parish responsibilities, another onerous financial burden. Additionally, the compensation the Commissioners paid after the lost lawsuit in 1881, resulting in the 1881 Act to borrow £7,000 for 50 years to meet the costs, led to Newborough's bad drainage state in 1900: there was little money to spend on drain maintenance, let alone improvements. At least Newborough was exempt from North Level taxes, and those Commissioners were responsible for the Welland Protection Bank from Crowland to Peakirk.

The 5th District, (The Great Porsand), was accepted in a similar situation regarding protection banks. By 1900, the Commissioners had accepted the responsibilities of the Welland Bank from Crowland to Brother House Bar from Normanton Estate, again a considerable financial burden. In comparison with the other North Level Districts, the 3rd District bordered the New South Eau and New Wryde banks, were maintained by the NLC as well as the 2nd and 4th District protected by the Nene Barrier bank.

Although these Districts paid North Level taxes scaled on the soil value and therefore productivity, benefits were considerable. Much of the land was owned by the Duke of Bedford and holdings were large, therefore internal drainage in these Districts was relatively good.

In Newborough and 1st District the burden of the Car Dyke and Folly River was such that until 1914 no improvements were done, only maintenance of drains, bridges and roads. Apparently, there was a continual process of lowering inverts of tunnels and bridges and taking a "spit" out of the drain bottoms providing minimal improvements.

During the war, activity increased, due to increased prosperity, but only further "cleansing" of drains, no improvement schemes. Joint schemes, by 1st District and Newborough Commissioners were proposed, but discarded from lack of funds.

A major repairing and strengthening of the Folly Banks began in 1919, becoming an annual job, clay being transported by light railway along the banks, using unemployed labour, with a grant of 75% from the Ministry of Agriculture and fisheries. In 1921, further trains and wagons, (Jubilee Trucks), were purchased to extend the work, still using unemployed labour. The industrial labour slump benefited the Commissioners when, between 1920 and 1926, they used hand-labour to clean out and improve many drains.

Completion of the new outfall sluice in 1859, and the subsequent lowering of the Cloughs Cross invert, together with improvements to the New and Old Wryde, the next few years enabled the 4th District to dispense with wind engines and offered the opportunity to lower their drains. However, only maintenance was performed between 1861 and 1900. Times were hard. Except for isolated areas, ground levels were higher in the 4th District and drainage adequate for grasslands, water was available from the Counter Drain and New Wryde and although the ground salt content was high, especially near to the River Nene, an adequate quality was retained for cattle drinking.

The minute books between 1904 and 1939 are missing.

The Tydd and Newton Drainage Commissioners had opposed the 1881 North Level Act. Promoters of pumping at Tydd, they found that these pumping arrangements had been removed from the Act, but after promises of improvement by the North Level, the Chairman, Alfred Coates, and the committee withdrew their objections, owing to the subsequent slump in farming the promises were broken.

The flood of 1912 again affected the area, high levels in the Main Drain preventing drainage. Representations were again made to the North Level, but nothing was done. Prosperity during the 1914-18 war prompted the Commissioners to consider pumping their water into the Main Drain, but no financial assistance was available.

The 1927 floods again caused difficulties, and the District Council was requested to raise Goredyke bank to prevent water overflowing from Gorefield Fen into Newton, (Gorefield Fen was independent of any Drainage Commission). Much of the area was highlands, consisting of silt and reasonably well drained. The problems lay in the poorer fens, and as taxes were levied per acre irrespective of productivity there was usually parochial difficulty in making money available. The Commissioners also still had a financial commitment for the Nene Outfall Cut.

The Leverington Drove Drainage Commissioners were in a similar position with high silt lands and lower clay land. The region was reasonably well drained except for small pockets, but the parochial attitudes were the same, particularly towards their neighbours, the Wisbech Northside Commissioners, whose boundary was along Leverington Common. One area drained by Gravity to the Main Drain, the other was almost wholly pumped, and there were always problems at Bellamy's Bridge in flood time.

Alfred Coates was Chairman of the Works Committee from 1892 until he died in 1927. It was quite common, because of the land ownership qualification in the areas, to belong to two or three Commissions, as well as being appointed to the North Level. In land drainage, the largest farmers, being the biggest tax payers, were often the most influential.

Much of the Wisbech Northside Commissioners' area was high silt land which had been farmed in Roman times, but many pockets of low clayland were difficult to drain and required long and tortuous drain systems to convey the water to the pumping engine at Rummers.

After the cutting of the Main Drain, the Red Engine and White Engine drain was reversed to flow westward to Bellamy's Bridge, instead of eastward to the wind engines at Wisbech, which were dismantled. Seadyke, taking water from the Murrow area, also discharged at Bellamy's Bridge. In flood time, water could pass down Highside Drain through the Leverington Parson Drove area. One can understand the parochial attitude of the two Commissions.

The flood of 1912 caused problems in low areas, which were waterlogged for long periods, particularly in the Guyhirn and Murrow Fens. Again, the advent of war assisted the Commissioner to improve drains by unemployed labour, Rummers drain being deepened and widened. However, local conflict between fruit farmers and arable farmers caused difficulties. On one hand, the water in the drains was required at a high level, in the latter's case, at a low level. To drain the lower land, the high silt land had to be cut through, lowering the water levels.

Floods in 1927, when many acres were inundated, partly resolved the conflict, a new steam engine driving an Appold centrifugal pump being installed at Rummers and the main drain improved.

Wisbech Northside was not regarded as a Commission contributing water to the North Level Main Drain, (A contributory Board), as it was wholly pumped except for small areas of highland still with some gravity discharge to the River Nene, and did not pay the North Level like the other two Commissions.

Transition from grassland to arable, accelerated by the 1914-18 war, also occurred in the areas, but not as rapidly as the North Level Districts. Much of the high silt land had been farmed for arable crops for centuries, it was the lower fens, more difficult to drain, which were affected by this transition with the attendant problems.

Without doubt, all the Commissions in the area of the North Level took advantage of the grants available from the Ministry of Agriculture for utilisation of unemployed labour, but hand work on the drains created problems. It was quite reasonable for unskilled labour to dig two spade depths, (spits), out of the bed of drains, but far more difficult and skilled to "shave off the" bank slope to produce a stable "batter". Many miles of small drains in the North Level area became steep sided and unstable in excessively wet periods. Improvements were achieved, but at a cost.

A Royal Commission, set up in 1927, reported on the administration and efficiency of Drainage Authorities and concluded that Main River Authorities should be set up to replace the numerous commissions dealing with the rivers discharging through the flatlands of England to the sea.

These new authorities were to be financed by a levy on County Councils and the various Drainage Commissions responsible for the drainage of the flatlands. They were also to be "Big Brother" to the drainage Commissions, with powers to set up new internal drainage Boards and take over Commissions which they considered ineffective. The resulting Drainage Act of 1930 set up the River Catchment Boards, whose area of administration was the catchment area of particular major rivers. They acquired powers to precept on both the County Councils and Drainage Boards, laying down the procedure which determined the boundary of the Boards. The boundary criterion was originally fixed within a line drawn feet above the maximum known flood level, but failed to define whether this level was tidal or freshwater. Resulting from the furore caused by this clause, the Medway committee, named after the first area to object, was formed of eminent drainage engineers, lawyers and members of the Civil Service. The committee's deliberations resulted in the Drainage Boards being designated "tidal" or "non-tidal", the criterion to establish the boundaries of tidal boards was a contour line at the level of the highest known tide in that area.

The new Act also required all Boards or Commissions, whether their inauguration Acts were rescinded or not, to levy two rates in accordance with land valuation, (productivity of the land), the Occupiers Rate to pay for works of maintenance and the Owners, rate to pay for works of improvement. This maintained the continuity of the ancient principles of 1258, when the owners were required to pay for improvements.

The whole of the new administration was controlled by the Ministry of Agriculture, who were empowered to give grants to Catchment Boards, the new main river authorities, for main river improvements and sea defences, but not to Drainage Boards or Commissions.

The North Level Commissioners and District Commissioners were unaffected by the Act, except that the North Level had to effect a land valuation of their area which both the North Level and District Commissioners used for their "laying" of the drainage rates.

The 5th District, (Great Porsand), became the Postland Drainage Board in 1928 under the 1861 Act, when the North Level Commissioners assumed responsibility for the River Welland bank from Crowland to Brotherhouse Bar from the 5th District, and Lord Normanton, whose land now became part of the new board.

At this time, the contributing Commissions changed. Tydd and Newton became the Tydd and Newton Internal Drainage Board under the Act. Sutton St Edmund and Sutton St James still remained in the Holland and Elloe Drainage Board, Leverington Parson Drove Commission became the Leverington Parson Drove Internal Drainage Board and Northside became the Wisbech Northside Internal Drainage Board. All these new boards were required to perform a land valuation and levy their rates in accordance with the Act; previously their rates had been levied on an acreage basis without taking into account productivity. The establishment of the areas with all the survey required, together with field by field valuation, was accomplished in less than two years, a remarkable achievement.

EXTRACTS FROM THE MINUTES 1900 - 1930
North Level Commissioners

1907 Agreed to pay travelling allowance to members, $^1/_6$d per mile. Press informed that their attendance was against the rules of the Commissioners. Permission given to erect a springboard at Church Lane Bridge on the Main Drain.

1911 Request from the 2nd District to pump into the River at Cross Guns. Resolved that men, wives and children should have a day out at Great Yarmouth to commemorate the Coronation.

1912   Ordered that the superintendent retain sufficient men during harvest time to meet all emergencies and pay them double wages.

1913   Tydd and Newton Commissioners request steam pumping at Tydd in flood time. Sir John Coode's report considered. Pumping at Cross Guns approved in principle. Gauge levels that mills and engines cease to work to be set at 10'6" above outfall sluice sill. Hire of Force pump to blow silt out of the outfall sluice.

1914   War - arrangements made with the Police to guard the outfall sluice. Agreed to rebuild Cross Guns public house and lease land for 99 years. Tenants of banks ordered to remove ducks and geese.

1915   Agreed to build a new house for the new superintendent at Cloughs Cross.

1916   Committee agreed to re-licence the Bedford Arms public house.

1917   Repairs to the sill of the outfall sluice by Siebe Gorman and Co., Divers.

1927   Agreed to take over the Welland bank in Postland from Lord Normanton. Resolved to inform the Ministry that the Nene Washland Commissioners had erected the cradge bank on the Nene higher than the 4ft allowed under the Nene Valley Act 1862.

1928   Postland Drainage Board formed - Lord Normanton's Estate sold.

North Level 1st District & Newborough

1st District Minutes Missing

1903   Whole board appointed Works Committee, (repairs to bridges only entries).

1914   Proposed joint pumping scheme, 1st and Newborough, (it is obvious that the clerk wrote out the minutes before the meeting and just filled in the gaps, very little detail recorded. H.H.Harris a Commissioner.

1917   Men directed to work until 4 pm on day work.

1919   Advert inserted that Commissioners require 16 men capable of tool work to repair Folly Bank. Commissioners hire light railway track for the bank repairs, (clay was dug from a borrow pit near the bank by hand and transported along the bank by light rail waggons, the bank being cored, raised and backed by hand).

1921   65% grant for using unemployed labour to raise Folly Banks, purchase of more light railway track, (Jubilee Track).

1922   Piecework men paid 3/- per week tool money. Unemployed used on drain works under grant scheme.

1929   Hiring North Level steam dredger to dredge Folly River. Charged for using water for the dredger from Peakirk Parish well.

North Level 2nd District

Minutes missing from 1754 to 1913

1916   New engine to be bought for £400 - erected by July 1916

1922   Popely paid £2.2s.0d per year for running the engine

North Level 3rd District

Minutes missing from 1754 to 1911

THORNEY DRAINAGE BOARD

1911   Jos Green to do carting for earth closets in the Town. Reported underdrains installed in the board's drain at East Wryde Farm ordered to be removed or pay way leave of 2/- per drain. Reported Thorney Dyke polluted by ducks which were ordered to be removed. Earth stored in shed in the yard for closets. Thorney River banks puddled with clay from brickyard. Commissioners' saw mill available for hire. Gleaving for eels not allowed in boards drains, (use of a fork with three thin, flat flexible tines). Drainage rate, water rate and additional tax, (sewage disposal, levied on the urban area of Thorney). No fishing to be allowed in Thorney River on Sundays. Reported no earth available for school closets, (phew!).

1912   Water inlets still required for cattle fencing. Dams installed so that arable land was unaffected. Small manual fire engine to be repaired. Dog in a Doublet public house now owned by the Board.

1913   Possible pollution of Thorney water supply by Peterborough City pumping sewage into the River Nene. Repairs to the hovel at the Dog in a Doublet, (the "loo").

1914   Foreman paid £2 per year to provide bicycle. Board provides mole catching service to ratepayers. Two full time men employed. Saw mill to be repaired.

1915   Report by CC on unsatisfactory water quality. Appointed a Mr Wood who recommended sewer flushing and ventilation, nothing on water. Earth closet collection passed to the Rural District Council.

1916   Resolved that all bridges and tunnels in the board's area were the responsibility of the owners. Labour still released in the summer for harvest.

1929   Great shortage of water, too low in Thorney River for syphon to work. Pumping with fire pump.

1930   (May), All outfall doors to be pulled immediately due to exceptional rainfall.

North Level 4th District

Minutes missing rom 1904 to 1939

North Level 5th District - Great Porsand

Minutes missing from 1754 to 1942

Tydd and Newton Drainage Commissioners

1913 It was reported that in flood time it was impossible to drain the district into the North Level main drain. North Level requested to pump at Tyd, (aftermath of the great 1912 floods). North Level propose to pump at Tydd End bridge - Commissioners object.

1915 Agreed to investigate pumping internally to drain the District.

1919 Resolved to request owners of Gorefield Fen to prevent water flowing from their area into Newton Fen, (Gorefield Fen was still independent).

1928 Requested District Council to raise Gordyke Bank to prevent water from overflowing from Gorefield Fen.

Wisbech Northside Drainage Commissioners

1914 Ordered that a new clap door be installed at Rummers outfall and Rummers drain cleaned out up to the railway at Sand Bank.

1929 H. Bain's report on the Eastern Anderson steam pump and Appold pump at Rummers. Gwynnes suggest a pump of 60 Tons/Minute.

The Steam Excavator

(Above), L to R:
The Ruston Rep.,
Bill Crowson,
Walter Jarvis, Tom Smith

(Right):
Steaming through Crowland

CHAPTER IX

Between the Wars - 1930 - 1940

The formation of the Catchment Boards in 1930 finally solved the difficulties associated with the River Nene. The numerous Commissions, each with their own interests, and the parochial attitude to mainte-nance had, by 1930, allowed the Nene to deteriorate into an apology for a main river due to siltation and bank deterioration, the result of bad maintenance and indebtedness - the great works carried out in the past still had not been paid for. The original income from tolls from barge traffic was lost when freight was moved to the road and railways. Much of the financial burden was carried by the Commissions protecting the River and its embankments. The safety of the North Level was inexorably linked to the state of the River Nene, as was the prosperity of Wisbech Port, where the quays and bank protection were crumbling, again due to inadequate maintenance.

After their first meeting in 1931, it was resolved to improve the River Nene from Walton Dam, below Wisbech, to Northampton. The Ministry agreed to grant aid, for the first time supplying three quarters of the cost, the rest coming from the new precepts on County Councils and Drainage Boards. The debts of the old Commission were paid off by the Government - the country was emerging from the farming recession.

The Catchment Board started dredging the River from Walton Dam to Wisbech in 1933 before the first hiccough of the new legislation was overcome. In 1932, the Ministry withdrew grants - but reinstated them in late 1933. Some 80,000 cu yards were removed from this length by steam bucket dredger, dropped into barges and pumped into holding lagoons over the bank. The banks were stoned and faggoted to produce the correct bank slopes and counteract tidal and ship propeller erosion.

The length from Bevis Hall to Peterborough was commenced in late 1933, completed in late 1937, 1,600,000cu yards being removed and the width of the river virtually doubled. The widening above Guyhirn was carried out by dragline, the rest with a bucket dredger, 400,000 yards being placed at the back of the North Barrier Bank for future bank strengthening.

The confined section of the river from the Town Bridge to Bevis Hall, the toe piles and beam of which can be see today, was began in 1937 by W C French, (Contractors - the present French-Kier on South Brink), and completed around 1941. Boring showed that there was a bed of silt and sand, in some places 40 ft deep, the top of the layer only about 8' below the new bed level after dredging.

Due to restricted of space, piles could not be tied back and concrete sheet piles and king piles were used, the head joined together with a toe beam forming an inverted 'V'. The sheet piles were 23ft long, 24" x 10" and the king piles 27' long, 12" x 12"; these were driven at 6' centres. Some 14,000 piles were driven over a period of four years, the works finally completed by 1942.

Part of this major undertaking included improving the flood reservoir of Whittlesey Washes; in 1930, the area flooded with almost every 'Fresh' coming down and was rapidly losing its original func-tion. A new sluice was erected at Stanground to let in flood water, an emergency weir constucted at Northey Gravels and a new outfall sluice at Rings End. The cradge bank was raised to prevent tide and low 'freshes' inundating the washes unnecessarily. Afterwards, the washes came into operation only on major floods without endangering banks.

Guyhirn and Dog in a Doublet bridges were rebuilt to conform with the new channel dimension which allowed the free flow of upland water.

There were two other major constrictions to flow, ie the high cemented gravel shoals at the Dog in the Doublet and Northey, (the latter was part of the Roman Causeway), between them they restricted the tide from reaching Peterborough except on major tidal surges.

Wisbech at low water, looking upstream from the bridge

*Wisbech at low water - piling completed. Stone pitching was placed behind the beam
and the material in front, dredged and taken away.*

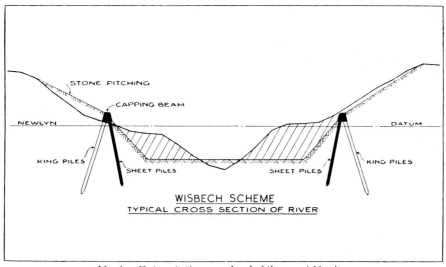

*Newlyn Datum is the mean level of the sea at Newlyn.
This definition is used to denote levels which are thus referred to a common base.*

Pile frames at Wisbech. The frame on the left is for driving king piles; a sheet pile is shown already in position, ready for driving at the other frame.

Wisbech at low water, before piling and dredging work has begun.

Wisbech at low water, showing piling and dredging work completed.

River Nene at Wisbech before piling and dredging works.
Note the old timber piles & shoals that can be seen in the bed

River Nene at Wisbech - pilling & dredging work completed

Wisbech Quay in the 19th Century

Wisbech Corporation Quay before reconstruction. Deterioration has allowed the filling to escape into the river.

Wisbech Corporation Quay - after reconstruction.

Completed section of the Corporation Quay, Wisbech.

Dredging scheme Bevis Hall to Peterborough. Dredging plant situated at Guyhirn.
The depot for disposal of spoil can be seen in the background.

Dredging scheme Bevis Hall to Peterborough. Widening below Dog-in-a-Doublet. The channel
shown on the right is the original channel. Preliminary widening has been carried out.

The River Nene below Dog-in-a-Doublet in 1924.

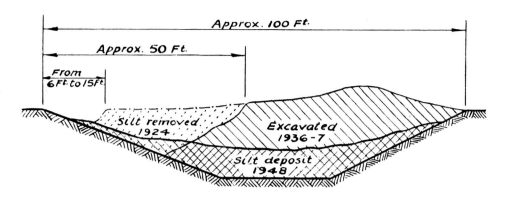

Typical section of the River Nene below Dog-in-a-Doublet Sluices,
showing the successive stages of the silting.

a) *The deterioration prior to 1924, when the channel was reduced to 6 feet in width.*
b) *The extent of the dredging carried out in 1924.*
c) *Improvements in 1936/7.*
d) *The silt deposits in 1948 as formed following dredging in 1943/4.*

Dredging scheme Bevis Hall to Peterborough. A Bucket Dredger at work, Guyhirn

River Nene at Guyhirn - after dredging

River Nene at low water - Northey Gravels, Sept 21st 1935

River Nene, at Northey Gravels, after dredging. Permanent depth of water - about 10 feet.

Dog-in-a-Doublet Sluice Mattress protection being towed to the sluices

Shaped Mattress protection - before sinking

1): Ice on the river, upstream of Dog-in-a-Doublet lock and sluices.

2): Ice on the river, upstream of Dog-in-a-Doublet lock and sluices.

Sea-going vessel, M.V. Peterborough Trader, upstream of Dog-in-a-Doublet lock.

*M.V. Constance H in Wisbech. This vessel was the first coaster to pass upstream to
Peterborough, following completion of works by the Catchment Board.*

It was upstream of these shoals that water was taken for drinking, via the Thorney River to Thorney township and the surrounding farms. A perpetual injunction was obtained by the Duke of Bedford in 1865, to prevent the removal of these shoals, subsequently passed to the Thorney Drainage Board in 1911.

To create the maximum freshwater flood storage in Whittlesey washes, it was originally proposed to site a control sluice and lock at Guyhirn, but this would have meant leaving the shoals in because of the injunction.

The only way of solving this would have been to agree to pump water to Thorney in perpetuity; however, it was finally decided to site the sluice and lock at the Dog in a Doublet and supply Thorney River by twin pipelines from the upstream side of the sluice, controlled by the Thorney Drainage Board. On completion of the structure in 1937 the injunction was removed, but it left the washes vulnerable to flooding from high tides and surges.

In my opinion, the siting of the new sluice was incorrect and short-sighted. Piped water was already available at Peterborough and Government money would have been better spent extending this supply to Thorney, thus obviating the need to distribute water through the Thorney Drainage Board district.

Additionally to the reason, there is siltation. The channel from Guyhirn to Wisbech has a far greater bed gradient than Guyhirn to the Dog in a Doublet, therefore that length of the river is susceptible to siltation.

The river, Guyhirn to Bevis Hall, is restricted between banks with little free access to land at the back, so much of the dredged material was placed on the washes between the channel and the bank, raising ground level to high spring tide level thereby reducing the overall capacity between embankments. This increases the velocity in the channel and helps to prevent silting, also the ability to discharge fresh water from the Whittlesey Washes at low tide, gives an ideal self-cleaning facility between Guyhirn and Wisbech. Major floods usually have an 8 ft surface fall at low water between Guyhirn and Wisbech Bridge, an indication of the channel restriction and a practical reason to site the sluice at Guyhirn.

However, the improvement to the River Nene lowered flood level, considerably reducing the danger to the North Level of bank over-topping or failure, a tremendous undertaking between 1933 - 1940 by the new Catchment Board and the Ministry of Agriculture.

In 1938, the Wisbech Town Quay collapsed, partly blocking the River. Wisbech Council could not get grants for repair, so the Catchment Board bought it, built a new quay by direct labour, obtained Ministry Grant Aid and a loan for the difference, and, on completion, sold it back. Wonderful co-operation from the Ministry and Catchment Board? The Catchment Board continued the improvement to Northampton, renewing locks and weirs and improving the river and by 1948, nearly all the tributaries had been improved as well - the flood water arrived in the Fens even quicker.

As for North Level, the prosperity created by the 1914-18 war soon diminished and despite the desperate flooding in 1912 and Sir John Coode's report, nothing was done. A series of bad years followed, with repeated requests from both the Contributing Boards and North Level 1st, 2nd, 4th and 5th Districts, for pumping improvements. Severe inundations were recorded in 1912, 1919, 1926, 1931, finally in 1936, when 6" rain fell in January and February on a wet catchment - there was just no spare money available, other than unemployment grants, nothing to the Drainage Board from the Ministry, only to the Catchment Board.

Agriculture was very slow to recover from the slump which officially ended in 1932, but by 1935 things were better and Boards were considering improvement. North Level members remembered their visit to the Middle Level Pumping Station at St Germans in 1924, the 2nd and 4th District had installed their own pump together with the Soak Dyke Pumping Co., (Arthur Gee and others). The floods in the winter, 1936, followed by a wet spring, plus the threat of mass legal action by the 2nd and 4th District farmers as a result of flooding, finally forced the North Level Commissioners into action. They commissioned a comprehensive report on the state of the North Level from E C Farron, a respected civil engineer from Doncaster.

Commissioned on 4th March, 1936, the report was immediately accepted by the Board on 15th October, but how to finance such a major scheme. The Catchment Board came to the rescue, agreeing in early 1937, to make short lengths of the channel to the proposed pumping stations, main river and apply for Main River Grant Aid. They also pledged £500 per annum towards the North Level's loan charges over thirty years.

Traditionally, the levels in any drainage system discharging to the sea were based on an arbitrary datum, usually the cill of the outfall sluice. It was possible, during no-flow situations in the summer, to relate land levels to water levels which were therefore related to the datum, with no relation between land level from one catchment to another, especially as even tide levels varied. In 1844, using the optical level invented in 1790, a new National Datum was created in Liverpool and the majority of the country levelled, setting up reference Bench Marks. This datum was based on low water ordinary spring tides, and the first step was the levelling of all graving docks in the ports around the British Isles. By the early twentieth century, Liverpool proved unsuitable, due to the wide range of low water and in 1921 a new national Datum was established in Newlyn, Cornwall. This was the point where the Atlantic tide met the British Isles. One half flows up the Irish Sea, the other up the Channel, meeting at Dover before flowing back to the Atlantic, so the mean level was far more consistent. All quoted ground levels in the country now relate to this datum.

The 1862 Nene Valley Drainage and Navigation Act produced its own datum based on an arbitrary bed level in the Wash; the Nene Valley datum was 26.96ft below Newlyn Datum, the North Level Datum about 12.0ft below - Farran referred all his levels to Newlyn Datum for the first time, which doubtless caused difficulties as all the "gauges" were to North Level Datum. Problems encountered by changing to Metric Gauge Boards make one deplore the loss of the old feet, inches and acres.

The maritime boys refused to change and all tidal levels still refer to the dock cills of the standard ports: as these were referred to Newlyn Datum, it was possible to work out the level of the tide related to the land, in other words, to give the tide level on Ordnance Datum Level.

Farran decided to base his design on the rainfall pattern between 1917 and 1936, choosing 1919 as the mean, comparing it with 1936 viz:-

	Jan	Feb	March
1919	2.91"	2.4"	2.13"
1936	2.50"	2.10"	0.84"

He calculated that the mean run-off was 7.4 cu.ft. per sec. and the maximum $11^{1}/4$ cu.ft. per sec. per 1,000 acres.

From his investigation into the North Level records, the recorded low water tidal levels at the outfall in 1937 were consistently 2 feet higher than in 1919. In the Catchment Board's inspection notes, in 1937 siltation was taking place in the improved channel, and extending the training walls at the Nene outfall further out into the Wash to reduce the suspended silt in every tide needed considering.

Doubtless, the outfall had silted between 1927 and 1936, to give this difference in low tide level.

Farran concluded by saying that the North Level was "flogging a dead horse" if they expected to prevent flooding of their low land by improving internal main drains and there was no alternative but to pump.

He recommended the following works all based on a design run-off of 7.4 cu.secs per 1,000 acres.

(1) Dog in the Doublet   120 tons per minute
(2) Cross Guns   200 tons per minute
(3) French Drove *(Booster Pump)* 270 tons per minute
(4) Protection Sluice, Tydd   800 tons per minute

Various main drains needed lowering and widening together with internal district drains.

He incidentally reported that the best way of dealing with the 1st District and Newborough was to pump at Wrights Drove into the River Welland, but, "In view of the complications which would ensue from pumping water from the Nene catchment area into the Welland catchment area, I have not pursued this idea".

Total cost, excluding internal boards drains, was £79,500. Ministry approval was obtained in the sum of £79,500 and work commenced almost immediately; however, the North Level Commissioners would not accept the need for the booster pump in the New South Eau.

Dog in the Doublet pumping station was completed in 1937, and Cross Guns in 1938, on the site of the old Cross Guns public house which was demolished. Tydd pumping station was finally finished in 1942. The main drain, the New South Eau, the New Wryde and drains to the Dog in the Doublet were all lowered and widened by the North Level.

It was obvious that Farran did not believe there was any future in considering gravity flow, emphasising this to the Commissioners, but with insufficient data to categorically press this point. However, he suggested that the North Level should inform the Catchment Board that their improvements upstream were affecting the levels of flow in the river and that deterioration of the outfall should be tackled, but the North Level was unlikely "to bite the hand that was feeding it".

It is interesting that W S Smith was the Vice-chairman of the Catchment Board, also chairman of the North Level Commissioners; the Thorney Drainage Board 2nd District and 4th District, doubtless he had considerable influence with the Catchment Board members. Smith died in 1966, after 57 years as chairman of the 4th District. In 1951, he and Arthur Gee were on the Catchment Board with Maurice Riddington - an influential trio.

The onset of the 2nd World War in 1939 probably accelerated the scheme, as food production was again of paramount importance; the highest priority being given to the supply of materials and the retention of skilled workers. A carpenter, named Tom Thrower, continued the steam pump, traditionally becoming pump attendant at the Dog in the Doublet.

The Farran scheme was a major step forward for the North Level, but did not cater for certain factors at the time of its design. Primarily, the system was for preventing surface flooding of low areas; without thought to maximum design water levels related to field drainage, perhaps influenced by the amount of grassland remaining in the level and its requirement for high water levels for cattle drinking and fencing.

Although land shrinkage was examined, the soil investigation only considered the Fen, when it was found that only 3 - 4 ft. remained and Farran concluded reduction in ground levels would be minimum. He was proved wrong.

His calculated drain sizes leading to the pumps were inadequate, causing a situation to develop almost immediately after installation where pumps had to be shut down, as there was insufficient water to feed them, although water was almost on the land within the District.

He made no allowance in his pump structures for intake levels to be lowered in the future, or even allowed space for the installation of further pumps, except at Tydd. The penny-pinching final design was strongly influenced by the chairman and members of the North Level who were, as farmers, recently emerging from a deep agricultural depression and were reluctant to saddle themselves with a large debt over many years, which was understandable, but extremely short-sighted. However, Farran and the farmers in the North Level should have realised that the developments in farming methods and mechanisation had already begun. The installed drainage system was outdated almost as soon as it began.

EXTRACTS FROM THE MINUTES 1930 - 1940

NORTH LEVEL

1933   Nene Catchment Board takes over responsibilities of Nene Outfall Commissioners and Nene Valley Improvement Commissioners. Main Drain being dredged by Contract.

1934   Differential Rating order approved. Association of Drainage Authorities proposed. No rates levied in year ending March 1933. Welland Catchment Board refuse to accept liability for the Welland bank.

1935   Cross Guns PH demolished. Stephen Fovargue, Sluice Keeper at Tydd retires after 56 years service - given pension of £1 per week. Stephen Watson appointed.

1936   Reported difficulty in discharging water at Tydd - Catchment Board works blamed. Farran appointed to look into difficulties. Farran's report accepted. Application made to the Catchment Board for Grant. Claims for land flooded in N.L.area.

1937   Catchment Board agreed to make lengths of drain Main River and apply to the Ministry for grant. They to contribute £500 per annum toward loan charges on a 30 year loan. Scheme to cost £97,560. Agreed to pump sewage from Peterborough's new works for £300 per annum. 1938 Contract let to Bomford and Evershed for Improvement to the Main Drain. Resolved to purchase new excavator. 50% grant obtained for Booster Pumping Station. Action against the Welland Catchment Board re the Welland bank was dismissed with costs. Action re flooding Farrow v North Level found in favour of plaintiff of £164 and costs. North Level joins Association of Drainage Authorities. Steam Dredger still in action. Improvements costs charged to owners rate. North Level takes over Postland bank.

1939   Cross Guns and Dog in a Doublet Pumps working after the thaw of heavy snow. Reported that Ministry grants available for mechanical works of drainage. Reported that the high level of water on Crowland and Cubitt Washes was endangering the North Level bank. 6th District Drainage Board formed.

1ST DISTRICT AND NEWBOROUGH

1934   Protests to the Ministry against the rating of land in Newborough by the North Level - took it to Court and failed. Second failure in Court.

1938   North Level pay for the Improvement of Highland Drain - 16000 cu.yds. excavated and the bed lowered 4 - 5 ft.

2ND DISTRICT

1938   Report to drain Mr Loweth's land sought from Farran. Resolved to dispose of the Steam Engine Pump.

THORNEY DRAINAGE BOARD (Old 3rd District)

1935   Foreman's report on Thorney River banks - agreed to repuddle. Agreed to the Dog in a Doublet lock with water supply under sole control of the Thorney Drainage Board. Thorney River banks piled with timber sheet piles.

1936   Injunction on removal of gravel shoals not to be removed until freshwater alternative in operation. Board Members elected for three years. Mole catchers still employed. Evidence given on the overhang of drain banks due to deepening by hand. Board fenced some grass fields where water levels were lowered.

1937   Landowners given permission for a temporary pump at the end of North drain. N.L. to fix gauge. Inspected freshwater pipeline at the Dog in a Doublet, recommended removal of injunction.

4TH DISTRICT

Minutes missing to 1939.

1939   The Engine at Turf Fen sold. Bishoplands Improvement scheme in progress.

5TH DISTRICT

Minutes missing.

LEVERINGTON PARSON DROVE DRAINAGE BOARD

1931 Resolved that owners of Gorfield Fen should pay £10.10s. to drain into the Little Cut. Scheme for unemployed to clean Board's drains approved on grant.

1939 George Tom Ward appointed Chairman. Resolved that the owners of Gorefield Fen should be allowed a rebate of £5 due to flooding.

TYDD AND NEWTON DRAINAGE BOARD

1936 Resolved to lower Willow Holt Tunnel after petition from owners and occupiers in Newton Fen.

WISBECH NORTHSIDE DRAINAGE BOARD

1933 Rummers Pumping attendant appointed at £2.2s per year.

1935 Report by Major Clarke for a new pump at Rummers and alternative pumping at Mouth Lane, together with a Booster pump at Folly's Drove for the Murrow area. Agreed a new pump at Rummers and a new pumping station at Mouth Lane.

1936 Opening of new diesel engined pump at Rummers. Chairman of Nene Catchment Board opened new Pumping Station at Mouth Lane.

CHAPTER X

The War 1939 - 1945

War finally brought agriculture out of recession, hitherto the nation had appeared interested only in cheap food from abroad, now it had to be self supporting. Agriculture between 1922-1937 received little support from Government, now it suddenly became the government's priority and grants became easily available.

Farmers got them for drainage schemes consisting of mole and tile drains and ditching. Drainage Boards got grants for maintenance and improvements.

Payments were made for breaking up grassland into arable, and for storage buildings. Men returned to the land to avoid conscription and the Land Army girls, conscientious objectors, criminals and prisoners-of-war provided extra labour. Derelict farms were hurriedly bought by industrialists, their sons installed as farmers.

Farmers and Boards in the North Level immediately grasped this bonanza after all the lean years. The War Agricultural Committees were formed in 1940 to supervise the breaking up and draining of grassland and act as drainage contractors, Farmers were given a 50% grant and a loan for the rest. Much of the draining work carried out was directed and not voluntary.

The history of underdrainage is as old as agriculture itself, reaching back to Roman times.

By 1938, the small dragline excavators were being produced by Priestman and Rustons, trenching tractors were imported and many Buckeye trenchers arrived from America. All these were quickly requisitioned by the "War Ag" , except those operated by Drainage Boards. Ford produced tractors for breaking up grassland and by 1941 the War Ag was in full operation. Records show that in 1941, 133,000 acres of mole drains were installed, 68,000 acres of tile drainage and 805,000 acres of ditching improvements completed, mostly in the eastern Counties. By 1944, they were running a fleet of 600 dragline excavators and 300 mechanical trenchers. Manufacture of excavators was not restricted by the war effort and even Drainage Boards required a release order signed by the Minister to acquire a new digger.

The development of the Priestman side arm and ditch shaped bucket meant farm ditches could be deepened to accommodate drains without taking too much off the sides. At this time, many drains were laid at the new bed level, so that farm ditches had to be maintained to a high standard, a somewhat forlorn hope.

The war created the fen vista of today, so unloved by conservationists. Many hedges were pulled out, ditches filled in to make larger fields, small wet areas filled in by levelling fields and drained mostly by edict from the "War Ag", to increase the acreage in production for cereals, not by "greedy fenland farmers" desecrating the Fenland, as is often believed.

The Fenland "Prairies" were created during the war and maintained and extended afterwards with government encouragement. The professionals in OFFICIAL conservation circles understand this, and encourage the enhancement of habitats without affecting drainage efficiency. Accepting the Fenland scene of today, they, by research and co-operation with countrymen, (the true conservationists), create and preserve areas which have become of scientific significance.

Many amateur conservationists, regarding themselves as experts, castigate authorities responsible for maintaining the drainage of the Fens. They might do better by investigating practical ways of improving habitats within the present regime, instead of concentrating on the past.

In one way perhaps, it was fortuitous that from 1939-1945, the North Level was completing its pumping scheme in a national agricultural improvement climate, with full government assistance, increased prosperity making it possible for most Boards to "pay their way" for their financial responsibilities. However, it was unfortunate that the lower water levels required in the Boards' drains to accommodate the farm drainage improvements were not foreseen, creating difficulties.

Within the North Level, two Boards received little or no benefit from the North Level scheme; Wisbech Northside still remained a separate pumped area, accountable for its own destiny apparently, and the 1st District and Newborough Board, which still had to drain 27 miles to Tydd. This region had always been the poor relation of the North Level, burdened for many years with the Car Dyke and Folley River and the Welland Bank.

Farran had recommended a booster pump in the New South Eau to cater for this area, but that was thrown out by the North Level Commissioners, probably because the channel was not designated "Main River" and therefore did not attract 75% grant. However, there was such protest from the 1st District and Newborough that it was added to the Main Drain Improvement at 50% grant and the pumping station was completed in 1939.

In 1930, the North Level had paid for the improvement of the Highland Drain to Powder Blue connecting to Slype Drain, into the improved New South Eau at "the Engine". This is possibly the only village to be named after the steam engine erected in the nineteenth century. Doubtless, the North Level Board members, except for the 1st District and Newborough representatives, had decided that it was prudent to see how the Main Drain system to Tydd pumping station operated, before adding further costs to a highly expensive scheme, especially having already invested over £1,000 in the area.

The members, doubting the efficacy of the booster station, were proved correct over subsequent years; the improvement to Newborough and the 1st District was marginal, but the increased water levels downstream of the pumping station inhibited the discharge from the Dowesdale arm, thereby affecting the flood discharge from the 5th District.

Farran's scheme incorporated changes in District Areas to balance the areas draining to the pumps. The Eastern end of the 2nd District was made into a separate drainage District, the 6th District drained along the Counter drain to the Dog in a Doublet Pump, the Eastern half of the 2nd District drained the same way, the Western half to Cross Guns. Half the 4th District drained to cross Guns, the rest, as before, to the Main Drain of Cloughs Cross. A quarter of Thorney drainage area was directed to Cross Guns, the remainder, as before, to Cloughs Cross, other Districts were unaffected, but derived considerable benefit from reduced water levels in the Main Drain. Because of the very flat gradients in the Fens, pumping made it possible to reverse the ancient gravity flow of East to West, which, because of land level variation, made it appear that "Engineers were able to make water run uphill".

The North Level commitment to the major scheme affected the Boards in the area by an increased rate and committed them to a ten year programme of drain improvement, so that all rate-payers received benefit from the overall expenditure. These local improvements speeded up in some areas, where farmers had experienced the considerable increase in crop yields due to good field and main drainage, but by the end of the war the water-level problems mentioned earlier were evident.

EXTRACTS FROM THE MINUTES 1939 - 1945

NORTH LEVEL
1945   Major slip in the bank at New Wryde at Murrow, decided to remove bank. Kingston died - appointed a Consultant. Culvert in Counter Drain at the Dog in a Doublet lowered. Jack Purser appointed Engineer and Superintendent. Stone pitching on Welland bank completed. Rainfall: July 0.86", September 1.87", October 2.31". First Engineers report to the Board. Retirement of Smith at age of 79 after 60 years service.

FIRST DISTRICT AND NEWBOROUGH
1944   Requested North Level to let water into the area during the summer -refused.

SECOND DISTRICT
1944   £100 charged to 6th District for facility to lead water into the District.
T HORNEY DRAINAGE BOARD (3rd District)
1941   Farran recommends improving Old Wryde drain. Old Wryde drain connected to Dowesdale bank by 2' pipe. Eastern Old Wryde still discharging to Tyd - being improved - "Faggots to be carted down the dredger trade with a quiet horse". New lifting gate with rabbit to be put in Old Wryde east of the road at Thorney. Italian prisoners used.
1944   Agreed that North Level take control of freshwater inlets at the Dog in a Doublet in drought time. Domestic water to Thorney to continue. No formal agreement made. "War Ag. second rate driver who is assisted or

perhaps accompanied by two Land Army girls, progress very slow", (Oh, what a lovely war).

1945 Frost and snow stopped work, but men went off thrashing. Men removing "racks", (rubbish dams in drains after snow melt). New 10RB excavator delivered.

4TH DISTRICT

1940 Reported that Mr Easinwood could supply lunch to the Commissioners providing they supply ducks and chickens - no lunch - port, sherry, biscuits and cigars instead.

1944 Holland CC take over road bridges over St James and Cox's drains. Reported St James and Cox's drain improvement scheme complete. Mill Ground pump installed for Cloot Drove area to be retained, (this was a 12" Blackstone pump discharging into St James drain.

Subsidiary drains scheme completed. Board paying £8 each for sinking wells in grass fields. Priestman Cub excavator purchased.

LEVERINGTON PARSON DROVE DRAINAGE BOARD

1941 Proposed that Gorefield Fen be included in the Board's rated area

1942 Gorefield Fen rated

CHAPTER XI

The Vengeance of the Elements 1945 - 1973
or The Cycle of Destruction

The agricultural prosperity created during the war, and the continuence of grants enabled the Boards and Districts of the North Level to proceed apace with improvements in their areas in order to take advantage of the new pumping scheme. By 1946, extra territories were being added to the original design areas of both Dog in a Doublet and Cross Guns pumps, but the deficiencies of the channels were also apparent as further acres of grassland were broken up and underdrained. Ratepayers were anticipating the same improvement as those fortunate enough to have land near the pumps.

The Thorney Board diverted the Ten Foot and Dairy Drove drains to Cross Guns and the Podehole area to the Dog in a Doublet, cutting through the clay hill at Tonehams. At this time Peterborough sewage was also pumped at the Dog and this was causing difficulties as the city expanded.

The 4th District had improved all their major drains, allowing some freeboard to land drains and widening on both sides to create $1^1/_2$ to 1 "batters", a very enlightened attitude.

1947 will long be remembered for the vengeance wreaked by the elements on the Fens. There were three weeks of very severe frosts that January; thick ice covered all the main drains, followed by heavy snow to a depth of 2 feet with more in the uplands. The thaw began on Monday, 10th March, with rainfall of 0.32" and 0.72" on the 10th and 12th; developing more rapidly after the 13th, the deeply frozen ground acted as if the entire Welland and Nene Catchment was paved, runoff was immediate. The thick ice on the drain inhibited plumbing and although drains were low, the rain and snow melt enabled pumping to start at Tydd and other stations, carefully, in order to keep the ice intact. It had been kept broken up at the intakes.

Water levels rose rapidly in the Main Drain, and the sluices at Cloughs Cross were closed; sandbags were placed at Tydd to prevent water entering the station on Sunday night, 16th. On Monday morning, water rose $4^1/_2$" over the windscreen platform, but the station managed to keep working. Similar problems were faced at Dog in a Doublet and Cross Guns with water levels just being held.

At Crowland the High Wash was covered in thick ice and the big gale on Sunday night, 16th, caused severe erosion to the bank, worsened as the Cradge bank was overtopped, spilling more water onto the washes. The severe gale affected telephone lines making communications difficult, if not impossible; there was no radio communication then. Large icefloes were coming down the River Welland, rigorously scouring the Deeping High Banks. By Thursday, 20th, the banks had been raised by sandbags. The water getting through Deeping High Bank was stopped, but was 2 feet above bank level in places. Under these freezing and dangerous conditions, this was a Herculean undertaking. The Welland and Nene were now in full flood - in fact every river in the country was in this state, so widespread was the sudden thaw and rainfall.

At 12.15 am, Friday, 21st March, the bank failed $1^1/_4$ miles north of Crowland. Also, water was running over Deeping High Bank into Deeping Fen. Rumour went that this had been "manually assisted" to relieve Deeping High Bank, but this has never been confirmed. However, this type of self-protection has occurred many times in the past in embanked areas. It happened one night in Somerset, despite patrolling the bank between Allermoor and Sedgemoor with loaded shotguns, Allermoor being flooded and Sedgemoor dry. The banks were breached in the early hours. It only needs a few spits with a spade and a speedy escape.

The 1947 failure rapidly produced a breach 60 yards wide and the water stored in the washes descended into the North Level. The following day, the Commissioners tried to confine the flooding within as small an area as possible; hoping to prevent the flood water overwhelming Tydd and the other pumping stations. Cloughs Cross sluice was boarded up and a stone dam placed in the South Eau at the Durham Ox, (The Engine), all slackers and sluices were closed and another dam put in Gold dyke to stop water going to Cross Guns. Flood water now covered all the Postland area and started to flow into Newborough down the main drains; these were hurriedly dammed off with stone.

The desire to protect self-interest resulted in interference with the dams and the South Eau continued to rise until water spilled out into the Thorney Drainage Board area. All culverts under the A47 and English Drove were hurriedly blocked and a controlled gap created with the New Wryde dam to let water to Cross Guns P.S. which by this time had broken the back of the internal thaw water.

The Nene Catchment Board took over the task of closing the breach, as the North Level were fully

Breach at Crowland Bank, March 21st, 1947. When the failure happened, the water level was at the top of the barrier bank.

Water flowing into the Crowland breach from the Cowbit Wash - March 21st, 1947.

Crowland Breach, 1947

*A temporary barrier of Tanks, used to close
the breach at Crowland - 1947*

(Left): Tank barrier at Crowland breach, showing protection by sandbags

stretched containing the flood water. This containment was to the detriment of Postland and Newborough, neither of which had pumping stations and their only outlets for their water had been blocked off.

The breach was partially filled using Buffalo Tanks, stone, tarpaulins and earth, but over the 29th, 30th and 31st, 0.75" of rainfall occurred and the Welland rose again. This rainfall came with gale force winds, worsening the situation and the ingress of flood water had to be restrained again to prevent submergence of the pumping stations. A battery of large portable pumps pumped flood water back into the Welland, water was being fed to the North Level pumps and some fed into the South Holland area, so that by 20th April, it appeared that evacuation was succeeding.

The rising River Welland now threatened the temporary repairs to the breach, which was already holding a 7ft head. At 7.30 pm on Friday, 11th April, the repair failed and water again descended onto the North Level. However, pumping and evacuation had lowered levels in the flooded areas, so the new influx could be dealt with. A cut was also made to connect the area North of Thorney to the Dog in a Doublet P.S., so by 21st April, the flood water was under control and going down. The breach was declared sealed, pumping from Newborough and Postland recommenced. A contract was let to Dredging and Construction Co. on 24th April, to complete the restoration and the Catchment Board withdrew. Flood waters had receded to below ground level by 3rd May, continuous pumping at the North Level PS's ceased, dams were lowered as the water went down. Some 21,000 acres had been flooded.

The previous improvements carried out to the river Nene, and the strengthening of the banks, successfully contained the flood down the Nene, but had it not been for the North Level's foresightedness in maintaining a rigorous campaign on the control of moles on the North Bank, a breach might well have occurred as the water rose in the Washes to within 18" of the top of the bank. The washes were full to capacity and with the gale's force considerable wave action occurred. However, there was little erosion, no doubt because of bank grazing policy. Summer grazing only by cattle was allowed, but sheep were encouraged through the year, so the grass mat was well tillered and shallow-rooted, the bank being well consolidated.

A continuous watch was kept on the Wisbech Northside bank and low places were sandbagged, although water reached the top of the bank at high tide, only minor seepage developed, insufficient to cause saturation. This bank

'Anybody there?'

was also grazed to the same standards and moles rigorously dealt with.

For earth banks to maintain their integrity, it is necessary to ensure moisture retention to achieve cohesion of the soils; drying out commences at the top of the bank, working its way down as evaporation occurs. However, it is the transpiration resulting from high rank growth which is far more serious. Twitch, (couch grass), roots can go down 16ft if the growth is not cut or grazed off. This moisture loss can be controlled from 12-18" in a normal year by suitable cutting or grazing methods.

During this major national flood, it was observed around the country that few well-grazed, vermin-protected banks which were overtopped suffered erosion on breaches.

In the Somerset grazing marshes in 1947, regular flooding by the silt-rich upland water was considered advantageous to growth and control of vermin, and the main river banks were constructed with long flat backslopes, heavily grazed and vermin-controlled; the same applies in parts of Yorkshire.

After closing of the breach, the banks were raised from Crowland to Brotherhouse Bar and work commenced on the Welland major improvement scheme. The Welland was tidal up to Peakirk; this scheme incorporated a tidal sluice and bypass channel in Spalding and an enlarged channel to Peakirk. These works were completed in 1953, and since then the Crowland and Cubitt Washes have never flooded, but came close to it in 1975.

Almost anything can be proved by manipulating statistics, such as a flood event will occur once in so many years, in the meantime, everyone is safe and it is a satisfactory return period for investment.

Unfortunately, the elements don't work that way, it is always necessary to improve protection to contain the last event plus a factor of safety. The exceptional weather circumstances of the 1947 floods were considered a one in 150 years event, yet despite this prediction, in 1975, similar flows were recorded on the rivers just with high rainfall on a saturated catchment.

The frost and snow in 1947 occurred on a wet catchment. 1946 was the wettest year since 1927, exceeded only seven times since 1868, so the ground was frozen very deeply, certainly 2ft if not more in places, similar to 1963.

The Postland and Newborough Boards took the brunt of the flood with part of the Thorney Board under water, but the other Boards draining into the Main Drain system also suffered badly. Their outfalls were blocked for a long period of the thaw, with no means of evacuating their water; low areas were under water and the rest waterlogged, especially the Tydd Board. Leverington Parson Drove Board were able to get some relief by passing water to the Wisbech Northsides pump at Rummers when that Board got rid of its snow melt. Later, some water was passed to the Rummers PS from the North Level Main Drain. The 2nd, 4th and 6th District were unaffected except by high water levels in the drains due to the controlled inlet of flood water to the pumps.

The high runoff and the water from the breach showed up the deficiencies of the pumping scheme as follows:

1. The runoff design figure based on a ten-year period of rainfall was greatly exceeded and was so again several times to 1968.
2. The inefficiency of the main channels to the pumps was obvious; water was on the land at the head of the pumped areas whilst the pumps were not working to capacity.
3. The floor level and weedscreen platforms were too low, no allowance having been made for the possibility of water on the land near the PS's.
4. The design capacity of the pumps did not allow enough reserve to cater for the severe restriction of output when pumping against the maximum flood level attainable in the Washes.
5. The siting of Tydd PS was suspect. In view of the age of the outfall and protection sluices it would have been more sensible to site it at the outfall sluice incorporating a new sluice with the structure and discharging directly into the River Nene, the old sluices being removed, but that would have cost more money!!

However, without these pumping facilities the North Level would have been completely inundated. The washes do their job admirably, but when the bank of this huge reservoir breaks, little can be done until the water goes down, except limit the extent by protecting the ends. A freshwater breach of this sort is far more catastrophic than a tidal breach. Although the reservoir is larger, we know the water will go down after about four hours. The major problem is the scour-hole at the back of the bank as the tidal banks are often higher. A breach in a major bank is an awesome spectacle.

In late 1946, the North Level were constructing a new sluice on the South Eau at Cloughs Cross; with the sudden thaw the contractor had to hurriedly remove the coferdam. This construction was to enable the existing sluice on the bridge to be removed and the false invert lowered. Even in 1832, allowances were made by far-seeing engineers to lower the sluice in the future. The North Level finally decided not to go ahead with the construction of the sluice. The aftermath led to government support for works of restoration and improvement with large grants available. All the main channels affected by flood water from the breach were cleaned out and scour-holes at the dam sites restored. The breach was finally repaired with 1,200ft of 40ft long steel piles, backed with imported clay, moved to the site on 3,500 yards of light-railway track along the bank. The 'Main River' channels to the PS were widened and deepened and an extra pump unit ordered for Tydd. (Fortunately the structure at Tydd had allowed space for two further pumps - foresight indeed.

In 1947, a shoal of dolphins, 6-8ft long, came up the River Nene as far as the Dog in a Doublet sluices. It was reported that most were destroyed by shooting!! Perhaps we are more enlightened these days.

The Land drainage Act of 1948 set up the River Boards, with powers to take over sea-defences. In many areas of the country, sea banks, although perhaps maintained by Drainage Authorities, were financed by a levy on the land they protected, a legacy of the original Act, not rescinded. Many were still privately owned by big estates, some River Boards, certainly in Somerset, required landowners to pay a lump sum to commute their liabilities; in some areas these liabilities affected land twelve miles inland. In Essex, no charge was made, one farmer's levy was over £1,000 per year.

The Nene Catchment Board took over the Nene banks in 1932, but the Welland Catchment Board

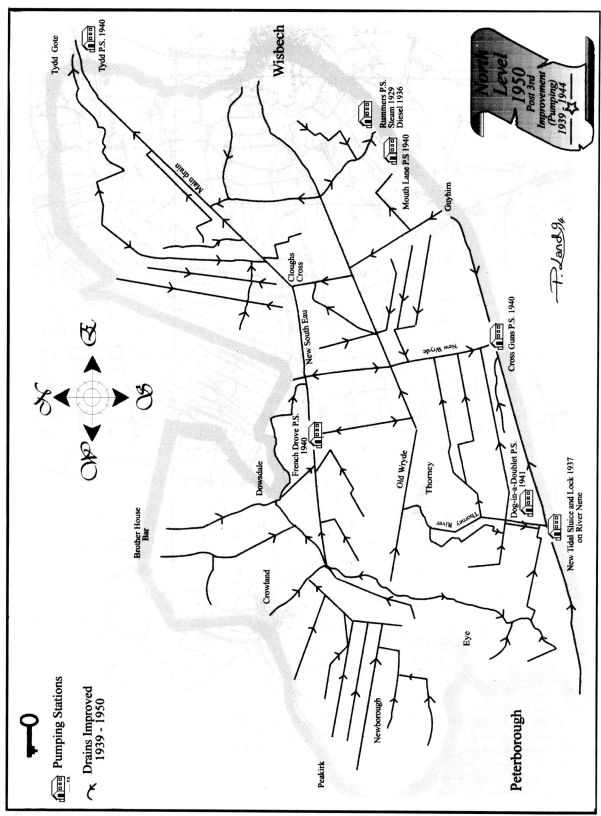

North Level Area in 1950.

refused to take over the Welland banks, so in 1947, the bank from Peakirk to Brothers house Bar was the responsibility of the North Level, additional to the Car Dyke and Folly river banks. Not until 1964, after the Water Resources Act of 1963, did the newly formed Welland and Nene River Authority accept the responsibility. The Welland Catchment Board had argued that they had taken over the Deeping High Bank and the cradge bank - how parochial can one get? It makes the breach even more convenient for the Welland Catchment Board!

Spring, 1949, was very dry and a severe gale for two days created the biggest "Fen Blow" in living memory. The black land in the Fens suffered, depositing some 4ft of humus topsoil in the drains. The restoration caused an increase in the occupiers' rate in 1950. In 1939, the depth of the peat areas in the North Level had shrunk to about 2ft; by 1968, most of this had gone, removed by root crop harvesting and "blows". In many areas the blue clay was being exposed at plough time. Wealthy farmers were resorting to soil-mixing to try to retain what humus soil was left.

1950 - 68 proved to be a very wet period, the annual average rainfall between:
1893 - 1912 was 19.88", 1917 - 1935 was 20.84", 1945 - 1955 was 24.99" and 1956 - 1967 was 22.78"

Winter, 1950/1, produced a flood greater than 1947, with similar conditions of ice and snow over Christmas. In November, rainfall was recorded at 4.36", December 1.81" then a sudden thaw; water levels in the Folly River rose 5ft in three days, threatening Newborough. The area was pumped 24 hours a day, from the 12th to 26th February. Rainfall from April 1950 to March 1951 was 32.09".

On record the Tydd PS operated for 2532 pump/hours and Cross Guns for 2450 pump/hours.

The pump inlet at the Dog in a Doublet was lowered by 4 feet in 1951, and with drain improvements finally connected with the Pode Hole area, obviating the need to pump this area into Bukehorn drain. Land-drainage water was finally removed by the improvement of Middle Drain from the PS to Northey road and the Catswater improved. The 6th District now discharged to the new drain to the PS; at the same time the North Level gave notice to Peterborough City Council that they would in future deal with their own effluent. An electric PS was constructed at The Dog in a Doublet to discharge into tidal water. It was unnecessary to feed water to Thorney via the Thorney River as piped water supply to Newborough, Postland and Thorney had just been installed.

In the 2nd to 4th Districts, the Counter Drain was deepened and widened to Cross Guns PS, necessitating considerable piling. The engineer obviously did not know how to deal with running silt. Tydd and Newton and Leverington Parson Drove Boards also suffered from lack of outfall due to high water levels in the main drain, and areas of Postland and Newborough went under water again. Wisbech Northside coped, but only just.

The elements again wreaked havoc in 1953, with the great tidal surge. The depression from two areas on Friday, 30th January, produced gale-force south-westerly winds which blew the water out of the North Sea, reducing tide levels by over a foot.

This low suddenly dipped SE, reaching 968 mb, and passed into the North Sea. By Saturday lunchtime, a strong ridge of high pressure developed in the west moving rapidly eastwards, bringing gale-force winds straight from the Arctic into the North Sea. In Orkney, mean winds of 90 mph were recorded with gusts of 121 mph, the highest an unprecedented 125 mph. These winds were felt all over the country, but so far were not phenomenal. In the south, however, gusts of 80 mph persisted from 8 am to 5 pm, preventing the sailing of the Queen Mary from Southampton. The herring-drifter fleet at anchor near Ullapool was swept into the fields where cattle normally grazed. During Saturday night, some four million trees were blown down in Scotland, as if felled by a bulldozer. These hurricane-type winds forced the water back into the North Sea. An estimated 15 billion cu.ft. of water was blown, raising levels 2 feet, this water being thrust to the right of the wind direction due to the rotational effect of the Earth. Locally, up the east coast, the Saturday midday tide did not ebb and the 1st February, Sunday morning, one was predicted as a full-moon spring tide. As the tide rose down the east coast, it was amplified by the surge heaped up and set in motion by the gale; a surge so monstrous, that some 6-8 feet were added to the predicted 8. The extreme depression in the North Sea falling from 992 to 968 mb, had the effect of raising water levels a further 12". The River Tees started to overtop embankments at 3.30 pm on the Saturday, high tide not being due until 4.45.

The depression which had been moving steadily, if slowly, east at 6 pm, veered south towards Heligoland, directing the wind towards the east coast. From the Tyne to the Wash, wind and sea made a mockery of the automatic tide-recording devices, ruthlessly destroying them. The defences of the East

Riding of Yorkshire were the first to fail, and by 9 pm water had reached Easinton village, a mile from the sea. Lincolnshire next felt the onslaught, the violence of the sea breaking through the dune defences and overtopping river banks. At King's Lynn, the tide rose 8.2ft above the predicted: one foot higher than in March, 1883 and two feet higher than in March, 1949. As the tide reached its peak at King's Lynn, the coastal defences were overwhelmed with devastating swiftness, as in Lincolnshire. The terrifying suddenness of disaster is strikingly illustrated by the story of the Hunstanton train, which left Hunstanton for King's Lynn at 7.27 pm.

"A bungalow floating on the crest of a wave struck the engine squarely on the smoke-box, damaging the vacuum brake-pipe, so that the engine became unmovable. Water was rapidly rising to the level of the seats, the lights failed, the engine fire was extinguished and from time to time heavy debris crashed against the coaches.

"For six hours, the engine-men and guard kept up the morale of the passengers, and at length succeeded in making a temporary repair to the brake-pipe, and by using the floor-boards of the tender, in raising steam sufficient to propel the train back to Hunstanton". Sixty-five people were drowned between Hunstanton and King's Lynn.

Wisbech and the North Level fared better. Fortunately, the wind was in the north-west, so the surge moved to the south of the Wash. Water came over the docks and the North and South Brinks and areas of the town were flooded. The water ran down Barton Road and the other North Brink roads like rivers, but little damage was caused. Fortunately, there was not much freshwater coming down the river.

Much has been written about the east coast floods, heroic deeds, tall stories, heart rending struggles for survival on that freezing January night. Contractors made money. Engineers gained experience or proved to be useless under pressure. The Catchment and Drainage Boards' staff were superb. Farmers did reasonably well out of compensation. Many were compensated through the Lord Mayor of London's relief fund. Like a lot of national disasters, the only people who lost out were the ones who lost their lives. One old boy who lived in a shack on the higher part of Canvey claimed that the tide-mark on the television set was where the water reached - he did not have electricity. The set had been passed round and many unscrupulous people had "two bites out of the apple". But there was still a considerable amount of money left for the Aberfan fund.

Most of the bank failures occurred where banks had not been cut or grazed. Water saturated the top 18" until they were fluid and flowed down the back, washing the back out and making the bank unstable.

The Ministry carried out a three-year research project in Essex in which I was involved. We steel-piled storage basins either side of a length of creek bank and simulated gradually increasing tide-cycles until the water came over the bank and the bank failed. With various types of sensors we found out saturation was occurring and water pressure building at the toe. We built new banks which were seeded and cut for two years, then tested. The investigation showed conclusively that earth banks must be cut or grazed regularly to avoid a tall rank growth of twitch. If this had been done, many of the bank failures could have been avoided. The science of Soil Mechanics has moved on since those days, but the ideal is still sheep grazing. I once employed a shepherd and supplied portable fencing to hard-graze a 21-mile length of major sea bank and very successful and self financing it was.

In 1953, the boundaries of the two contributing Boards were altered. The Tydd Internal Drainage Board took over Sutton St Edmund and Sutton St James and gave up the Newton area and all the new area draining to the north side of the Main Drain. Gorefield Fen was still separate. The Tydd then set about draining these new areas, improving Sutton St James drain and Denhams into a cleaned out Shire Drain. Sutton St Edmund was badly drained, being at the top of Holland Elloe Board's area and mainly grassland. The Straight Reach was improved to reverse the flow from north to south to the Main drain and the connecting cross drains were also improved. Les Pooley, the North Level Superintendent, who retired when I did, drove a 10RB then, and recalls that the bed level of Straight Reach was lowered by 5ft and had to be pumped during excavation, as the North Level would not lower the main drain. Apparently, they pulled out the foundations of the old steam pump and drew the wooden cut-off timbers which were perfect; some became the work bench in his garage. He also pulled out the foundation of the old wind engine. He particularly remembers this drain as he and his two banksmen supplemented their wages by collecting eels, when the water was pumped down from each bucketful of dredgings, and selling them on the Wisbech market. Harry Merral, the Board's foreman, tried to jump the drain using a long-handled hodding spade and fell in. He surfaced, wearing a long drooping moustache of cott! Les was the dragline drive for Tydd, Leverington and Wisbech Northside Boards until 1960, becoming superintendent in 1970; he was regarded by Rustons as one of the finest drivers in the country.

Winter, 1954/55, was another flood period, with an annual rainfall of 31.8". There were three sessions of non-stop pumping at the stations, with Tydd operating 2200 pump/hours. There were now five pumps at Tydd with a total capacity of 1000 tons/minute. The 4th District embarked on a scheme to divert most of their area through a new cut to the New Wryde through Bishoplands, and give up Peakirk Drain and Vermuyden's Drain to Guyhirn. They also cut three new drains to the Counter Drain; adding a further area to the Cross Guns pumps.

Resulting from the imminent danger threatening the North Bank in 1947 and subsequent floods, the River Board raised and strengthened the tidal banks from Wisbech to the Dog in a Doublet and dredged the river in 1955; the North Level offered a third of the rents on the North Bank to the River Boards.

Another wet year was recorded in 1958, a summer flood, when 16.26" fell between June and September, more serious for farming than a winter flood. Weed growth was at its height in the drains, restricting the flow to the pumps. Water came onto the land at the head of the pumped areas: Newborough and to some extent Postland, were flooded, the dreaded cott was at its peak and the Norfolk reeds had not been cut. Hired Boards' machines were used to pull out the worst cott blockages, but the Norfolk reed had to be cut with scythes and river knives by hand. At a station in Essex, about the same size as Cross Guns, one pump worked intermittently and water was on the land three miles upstream due to the flow resistance of Norfolk reed; which does not fall flat when flows occur. By September, the whole area reached saturation and much of the cereal crop was standing in water. It was a difficult harvest!

The worth of underdraining proved itself that year; the drained land was rid of surplus water and those farmers were able to get most of their crops off. The rest stayed in the ground or were dug by hand. Many combines were towed by tractors, and reapers hurriedly rejuvenated. I remember seeing fields of flooded stooks. The land took several years to recover from the consolidation and subsequently there was an upsurge of under-draining throughout the country.

In 1959, the North Level made major improvements to the Main Drain and South Eau to the booster pump, the New Wryde was improved to Thorney and they were now able to take full advantage of the lowered invert at Cloughs Cross.

Newborough again went under water in 1958, but in 1957, Newborough and the 1st District had combined to form the Newborough Internal Drainage Board. The combined Board had a greater rateable area, making it easier to carry out improvements, so they immediately proposed a major improvement scheme, and invited Stirling Maynard from Peterborough to carry this out; they produced a scheme in 1960, a very long time. It was not accepted by the new Board members on the grounds that it would lead to over-draining. I imagine the real reason was that they could not afford the extra money required. There were a lot of small farmers, compared to other parts of the North Level. The original scheme was estimated to cost £47,912, but when finally passed by the Board in 1962 the figure had dropped to £30,226. With 50% grant, the Board was required to finance £15,113, equivalent to £1.35 per acre per year excluding interest. The North Level had continued their improvement from the booster pump to the Hundreds Drain outfall to the west of the Engine Village to cater for the Newborough work; the low areas, which regularly flooded, waited until 1965 for completion.

River Nene in 1963

Laying explosive charges in an attempt to break the ice & open a channel for shipping.

Tidal River Nene at Sutton Bridge, showing floating ice, 5-6ft thick

1960 was another wet winter with 13.53" between November and January. The 1960 annual rainfall was 27.46" and Newborough was in some difficulty again. Postland was all right as the improvement to the South Eau gave them the extra benefit of lowered flood levels, as did the downstream Boards except Wisbech Northside, where conditions were worsening because of the run-off from increasing development around Wisbech.

1961 also saw the Act setting up the River Authorities which combined the Welland and Nene into the Welland and Nene River Authority and finally allowed the Welland, Car Dyke and Folly river banks to be taken over. The North Level retained the grazing rights on the Welland bank.

The surface water from new developments in Wisbech was causing embarrassment to both Wisbech Northside and Leverington Parson Drove farmers. Both Boards embarked on major schemes to alleviate the problem. The Leverington Internal Drainage Board, formed in 1961, now incorporated Gorefield Fen and proceeded to improve Highside drain from Wisbech along Leverington Common and down to the Main Drain at Gorefield and Wisbech Northside from Wisbech along Town Ten drain to Rummers Pump. All this caused bitter disputes between the arable and fruit farmers, the latter requiring high water levels in the drains, the former requiring the opposite. However, development surface water had to pass through both areas to the pumps; the resulting delays meant that the improvement was not completed until 1966. Nevertheless the Board had gone ahead electrifying the old steam engine pump, the first electric pump in the North Level area, the old steam engine sold for £50.

1963 was the year of the big freeze, the sea froze, so did rivers; temperatures plummeted and the frost penetrated 2'6" into the ground. Hares were frozen to the earth, birds frozen to the trees. We had a floating PS in Essex and a 24 hr. ice breaking team in action; the ice 3'4" thick. I inadvertently gripped a handrail and ripped the skin off my palm, those were Arctic conditions. There were foolhardy exploits, from Michael Osborn walking across the Nene at Wisbech, to a friend of mine driving an Austin 7 across Hanningfield Reservoir. One poor old boy at Burnham-on-Crouch drifted up and down the river with the tide for three weeks when his houseboat broke adrift, supplied with food and water by helicopter. Ice like this is a tremendous danger in the Fen drains and rivers when the thaw starts; on the rivers ice floes are too big to go between the piers of the bridges, forming great dams which have to be blasted apart; as happened at Guyhirn and Sutton Bridge. For this reason all bridges should be clear span. It may only happen once in a lifetime, but with disastrous results.

In the large Fen drains, pumping must be restrained to keep the ice whole as long as possible. I have seen slabs of thick ice flat against a weedscreen completely inhibiting the pump. With care, the ice will follow the water level down before breaking up. At the Dog in a Doublet sluices, a gang worked 24 hrs. a day breaking up floes and steering them through the lock.

In 1963, the Ministry set up the Field Drainage Experimental Unit, to try and consolidate the various methods and theories related to underdrainage around the country. They proved that underdrains suffer severe deterioration and siltation if submerged for more than 48 hours. This signalled the death knell of the old principle of drains on the bed of the ditch. Boards in the North Level were now forced to allow tile drains directly into Main Drain. This had been resisted for years and led to difficulties when mechanical maintenance took off, also to endless complaints in the North Level in wet periods.

In 1964, the North Level lowered the intake of the booster pump as a result of the South Eau Channel Improvement; when the Hundreds Drain improvement was completed in 1965, the situation was bettered in Newborough, but their water still had to go to Tydd, so they could attain the new criteria for underdrainage. Again, Newborough was the "poor relation" of the North Level; little underdrainage was done, therefore yields were lower.

In 1965, the main drain was completed, the spoil banks removed, new bridges constructed at Tydd Gote, Tydd Fen, Kirkgate and New Cut, on the South Eau. All these were taken over by the County Council. The Main Drain functioned much better, but it meant water was getting to Tydd PS much quicker; however, the Tydd and Leverington Boards also benefited, as with their internal improvements, their water was being pumped before water from upstream arrived. Much of their ground was higher and could take advantage of underdrainage, except for North side where conditions were worsening as the pumps could not be lowered.

The late 60's and 70's were as wet as the 50's. The North Level system was again tested in the winter of '65 with rainfall in November and December of 2.53" and 4.15". The runoff involved ten days of 24 hr pumping at all stations, the system was definitely struggling. Summer, 1965, 14.5" of rain fell between June and October, with 4.45" in August, another disastrous wet harvest, the whole area waterlogged. All Boards' machines, and some hired, worked flat out removing weed blockages. All stations were ordered to pump as low as possible with the mistaken notion that water would clear quicker. It was thought land furthest from the pumps was not receiving the same benefit although paying the same rates, something needed doing.

Whilst members were considering the situation, it began raining in April, 1968; by July the ground was well saturated. On the 10/11th July, a vicious low pressure area, like a miniature tornado, swept up from the south, passed across the North Level, rushed suddenly north-eastward across South Holland and into the North Sea. In twelve hours, 4.15" of rain fell in the North Level and in south Holland , giving total rainfall in July of 5.86". Most land in the North Level was flooded or completely waterlogged and growth in the drains was at its height. It was worse than the floods caused by the Crowland breach.

The previous winter, the outfall pipes at Cross Guns were leaking badly and work was underway to replace them. Work was stopped, but the station could not function to capacity. Winter, 1966, the outfall sluice was leaking and the North Level decided to renovate completely, cost: £27,000. Fortunately, this work was completed in early '68. It would have been catastrophic if that work had been underway during that fateful summer.

Weedscreens at the pumping stations had traditionally been cleaned by hand using long-handled cromes; the weedscreen platforms were only large enough for a nominal amount of weed before it was carted away by wheelbarrow. Certainly nobody anticipated the need for mechanical access to the weedscreen platform. The residue of floating weed after mechanical weed clearance, plus the past year's rodings which floated off the banks, all arrived at the PS's. Teams of men worked 24 hour days clearing weed off the screens and removing it with tractors and trailers where viable; floating booms were placed across the main pumping channels and machines with weed-rakes cleared as much floating weed as possible. The dreaded "Cott" was in full growth; under flood conditions, it rolls along the bed creating huge 'sausage rolls' with cotton wool consistency, which can only be removed by machine; if this algae gets to the PS, it forms a weir at the foot of the screen and prevents the pumps working to their lowest level. It can only be abstracted by hand a little at a time, being difficult to break up and extremely heavy. Some screens are 14ft long and the rakes, (cromes), had to be pulled up the full height.

Between April and October, 23.51" of rain had fallen and the annual figure was 30.14". All Boards agreed unanimously that something had to be done. The North Level, with the great Dick Berry in the chair, decided on immediate action. He proposed that Harold Clark, engineer to the Welland and Nene River Authority, prepare a scheme for the whole North Level and that all Boards should become one body. I had known Dick since 1966, when he was Chairman of the River Authority Works Committee. He was a tremendously practical man of few words, but with immense drive.

Within six months he had agreement from all Boards to a new overall pumping scheme and to a 4(1)B order from the Ministry to amalgamate all Boards in the North Level into a single authority to be known as the North Level Internal Drainage Board. There were objections by the 6th District whose area included part of Peterborough, including Perkins. He persuaded the River Authority to take over the responsibility for Peterborough surface water and remove the development area from the proposed North Level rateable area.

Survey of main drains commenced with both North Level and River Authority staff and proceeded at great pace, a preliminary report was ready early 1970, and submitted to the Ministry which ordered each pumped area to stand in its own "Worthwhile Test". They approved the design criteria, vastly different from Farran's scheme in that a run-off of 20cu.ft. per second per 1,000 acres was allowed, compared to 7.3, and pumping levels plus channel design were to give a freeboard of 12 inches to land drains laid 3ft below the lowest land in each catchment at full flow. Farran's plan was only to prevent surface flooding.

Harold Clark's scheme had envisaged pumping at Cloughs Cross, but Dick Berry was not particularly in favour, despite its merits. However, as each part of the scheme was to be submitted separately, part I, the proposals for Newborough, Postland and Padholme, (6th District), went ahead.

The River Authority enmained some 2.65 miles of existing ditches at Postland, 2.58 miles at Newborough and 1.25 miles at Padholme; existing Main River at the existing stations were also extended. The significance of enmaining was that Main River works attracted a grant of 71% whereas IDB grant was only 50%. In these cases however, there were other reasons: putting more water into the Welland, especially in flood time, was an extremely sensitive matter, as it could affect Deeping High Bank and might cause the Crowland Washes to flood. These had not flooded since the Major Welland Scheme and were by now fully cultivated with their own drainage PS. Passing control of the new stations to the River Authority meant that they could control their discharge in flood time, not however, a satisfactory solution for the North Level.

The Padholme pumping station was to be designed to cater for the surface water from Peterborough and paid for partly by the WNRA, partly by Peterborough Development with a Ministry grant. The 6th District drainage was accepted to the pump.

In 1972, I was sent down to the Fens to combine the two River Authority Fen Divisions, also to set up the organisation required to supervise the North Level Major Improvement scheme. I was unaware until much later that Dick Berry had influenced the move which I would not have thanked him for at the time.

The 4th Major Improvement Scheme in the North Level began in August, 1972, four years after the '68 flood, followed on 1st April, 1973, by the formation of The North Level Internal Drainage Board, responsible for the drainage of some 97,000 acres.

The following were the appointed members of the New Board.

Dick Berry	Chairman
Gordon Wilson	Vice Chairman & Tydd IDB
Norman Manser	Newborough IDB
Philip Whitsed	" "
Tom Darby	" "
Alan Ashpole	Cambs. CC
Jack Hemmant	2nd District
Roy Fisher	"
Arthur Gee Jnr.	Thorney IDB
Ernest Hurn	"
Arnold Hemmant	"
Philip Berry	4th District
Harry Ward	"
John Green	"
John Clarke	Wisbech Northside IDB
P K Coupland	" "
Bill Bliss	" "
Peter Allit	Leverington IDB
Graham Ward	"
Herbert Carter	Tydd IDB
David Coats	"
Les Roney	"
Bill Banks	Postland IDB
William Riddington	"
Bill Gutteridge	6th District

Jack Purser was the engineer and Roy Wedley the Clerk and Financial Officer; there were two assistant engineers, Rodney Hunt and Peter Mossop. It was a strong and experienced Board, consisting mainly of Chairman and Vice-chairmen of the constituent Boards and was destined to carry through the Major Scheme.

EXTRACTS FROM THE MINUTES 1945 - 1972

NORTH LEVEL

1949 Settlement on breach restored to 23.00 OD Liverpool. Costs related to the Breach:

Emergency works £24,855
Repairs to breach £72,100
Strengthening bank £171,773

1952 Discussion with the Clerk as to suggested lay-out of the History of the Constitution of the North Level Commissioners and their subsequent activities to date. Clerk reported that he was finding that his researches for the material of the preparations of the History was taking much longer than he expected. (That's putting it mildly).

1953 No support from members for Bi-centenary Meeting as members had to pay for their own lunch! Twenty-three to attend! Roding and shearing complete, Allen scythe used on the bank. New Tydd engine and pump completed. Proposed improvement to main drain and South Eau and removal of banks. West Bank road, Crowland taken over by Holland CC. Removal of South Eau banks, grant-aided.

1954 Welland bank tolls removed for one year as toll house untenable.

1955 Average annual rainfall for previous ten years was 24.99", this year 31.80", three periods of non-stop pumping, pump hours:

Nov: Tydd 1038 Booster 471
Dec: " 1163 " 570

1960 Discovered a false sill three feet above the brick invert at Cloughs Cross.

1961 Rainfall: Oct 4.47", Nov 3.54", Dec 4.00", Jan 2.98", Tydd 1250 hours, Cross Guns 740 hours. New Land Drainage Act.

1966 Rainfall: Nov 2.53", Dec 4.15", non-stop pumping for ten days over Christmas, not necessary to pump at French Drove, (Booster PS). Portable 6" pump purchased for use during excavation for the New Wryde Im provement scheme. Committee agreed to renovate the Outfall sluice at a cost of £27,000 with 85% grant.

1968 Considerable leakage to outfall pipe at Cross Guns. Approval received for a new sluice at Cloughs Cross. Severe storm on 10/11th July - growth at its height. Own and hired machines working overtime pulling out weeds. Tydd and Cross Guns pumped every day from July to September, Work on Cross Guns pipeline suspended. Cloughs Cross dam piles removed twice. Proposed mechanical roding before harvest - compensation to be paid. Welland and Nene to investigate Major Scheme.

1969 Decided not to proceed with Cloughs Cross sluice. Rodney Hunt appointed assistant engineer. Dick Berry chairman of the North Level. Resolved to ask WNRA to prepare a scheme of amalgamation.

1970 More slips in the Main Drain, one at Kirkgate bridge taking down the abutment. North Level surveying for Major Scheme. North bank improvement scheme complete. Hired Akerman Hydraulic machine with weedbucket and 46ft reach.

1971 Demonstration by ADA on water-weed control at Yaxley. Ministry reported that each catchment of the Major Scheme to stand on its own merits. Appointed day for North Level Internal Drainage Board to be lst April. Mr Clark reported that much of the preparation of his report was done in his own time! What an honest chap!

1972 Roy Wedley appointed Clerk, A Atkins appointed Pumping Station Superintendent. Ad hoc committee formed for Major Scheme.

1ST DISTRICT AND NEWBOROUGH

1955 Surveyor sacked for embezzlement.

1962 Major Improvement scheme proposed at a cost of £46,000 with 50% grant and a twenty year loan, subsequently revised to fifteen years.

1965 Hundreds Drain scheme completed. Grant not paid on outfall sluice and other sluices. Welland River Board to put in a new fresh-water lead and sluice valve at Peakirk Bridge approved.

2ND DISTRICT

1947 Connection to 2nd District from Thorney River made.

1950 Dog in a Doublet intake lowered.

THORNEY DRAINAGE BOARD

1949 Fen blow put 23' in the drains cleaned out by hand. Dog in a Doublet PH sold for £1525. Thorney Drainage Board charged £52/yr. for water to pass through 2nd District. Dredging scheme for old Wryde approved with 50% grant.

1963 Six residents around Thorney Green complained of children using it as a playground. Residents told by the

Board to keep them off.

1972 Hired long-reach Hymac machine with Dutch Herder weedcutting bucket.

4TH DISTRICT

1946 Machine to work on both sides of the drain for improvements Nos 5 and 6 drains.

1947 No mention of the major floods.

5TH DISTRICT

1946 Freshwater intake from the Welland renewed.

1952 Proposed to transfer Crowland to the 1st District.

1962 Cards issued to employees on Weil's Disease caused by rat bites. Agreed to supply scythe blades previously supplied by the men.

1966 Men still away harvesting.

1967 William Riddington - Chairman. 10th July, excessive storm. Rainfall
July 6.11",
June, August and September collectively, 14.4" - the highest since 1829.

WISBECH NORTHSIDE DRAINAGE BOARD AND WISBECH NORTHSIDE IDB

1954 Resolved to erect auxiliary pump in Folly Drove Drain.

1955 Boiler and old steam engine removed from Rummers, sold for £50.

1960 Reported that a tractor-driven pump was erected at Folly's Drove. Electrification of old steam-driven pump at Rummers complete.

1972 12" Diesel pump installed at Folly's Drove to replace tractor pump.

CHAPTER XII

Fourth Major Improvement

Being responsible for the Main River part of the North Level Major Scheme, I was able to have some input into the detailed design and although the Clark Scheme had been approved, it was on the basis that each section must be submitted in detail; it was at this stage that we were able to alter the design criteria.

By 1973, intensive survey had shown the lowest land to be catered for in each catchment, so channels and pumping levels were based on the underdrainage requirements of that low land. At the maximum run-off of 20 cu.ft/sec/1,000 acres the following gradients and freeboards were allowed as a guide at this stage.

(1)	Arterial Main Drain	1 in 10,000	(0.01%)
(2)	Arterial District Drain	1 in 5,000	(0.02%)
(3)	Farm Ditch	1 in 2,500	(0.04%)
(4)	Land Drain	1 in 666	(0.15%)
(5)	Depth of Land Drain outfall from Ground level	3'3"	(1.0m)
(6)	Freeboard from max. W.L. to the Tile Drain	6"	(0.15m)

Because we had the detailed survey and knew the soils we had to deal with, by using the Soil Survey of GB, and some land survey to assess the remaining depth of peat, we made a further allowance for settlement of the ground from 6" (0.15m) to 18" depending on the peat. This was based on peat shrinkage of 1" per year over the life of the scheme or the actual average thickness, whichever was greater.

By using these standards, we arrived at the ideal maximum level required at the pumping station, (we were by this time going metric), eg:

		LEVEL		
Lowest Land Level			=	0.3 MOD Newlyn
Max Length of L.D. 133M at 1 in 666	=	Less 0.2M	=	0.1 MOD Newlyn
Depth of Land Drain @ 1m	=	Less 1.0M	=	-0.9 MOD Newlyn
Shrinkage, say 0.3 M	=	Less 0.3M	=	-1.2 MOD Newlyn
Freeboard to Land drain	=	Less 0.15M	=	-1.35 MOD Newlyn
Farm Ditch 750M at 1 in 2500 say 0.3M	=	Less 0.3M	=	-1.65 MOD Newlyn
Arterial District Drain 7000M at 1 in 5000	=	Less 1.4M	=	-3.05 MOD Newlyn

Therefore maximum level at full flow conditions at the pumping station should not exceed a level of -3.05 M. All land in the North Level was to have water levels suitable to maintain underdrainage systems.

Research has been done throughout the years to arrive at formulae associated with flow in channels and coefficients of friction for different materials and growth established: much of this research, however, was carried out in the uplands. In the flatlands, where gradients were minimal and therefore velocities very low, the formulae were really inapplicable, but gave a guide to the channel size required, which then had to be adjusted for each different situation of soil and likely growth conditions. The channel sizes on Farran's scheme were inadequate to get the water to the pumps. Also it is of first importance to contain a summer flood when growth is at its height.

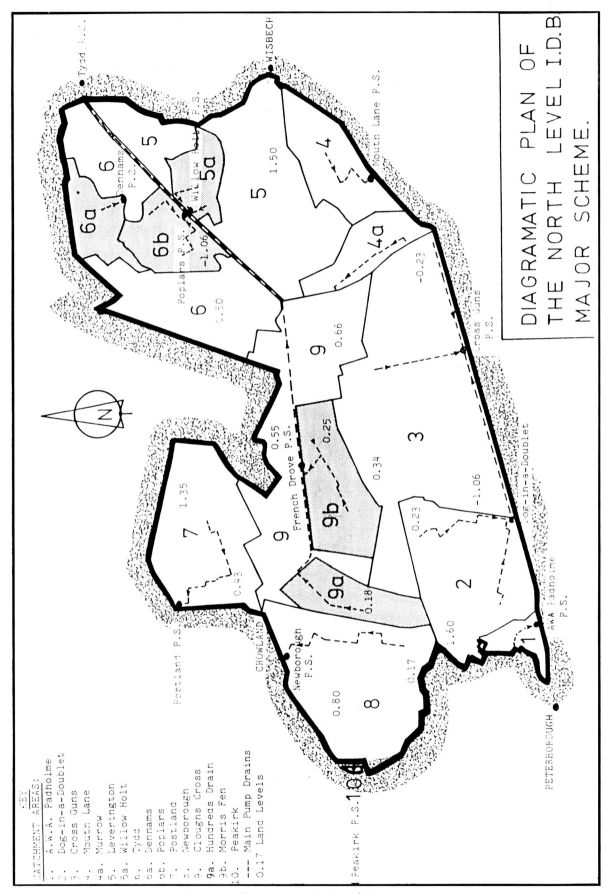

Diagramatic Map of the 4th North Level improvement

We used various coefficients in the North Level based on our experience and as the overall scheme progressed, altered these after monitoring flow as pumping stations came on line and mechanical weed-cutting became more efficient. All the North Level pumped catchments were designed on the above basis, it soon became evident that we had reached the ultimate drainage depths to which Batter, (Bank Slopes), would remain stable and any future lowering of the water-level would have to be achieved by considerable widening of the drains, not deepening. However, channels deteriorate over the years, and all pumping stations were designed so that pumping-level could easily be lowered by 0.6 M".

In 1973, Harold Clark retired and Geoff Bowyer presented a revised overall scheme to the new Board which was accepted in early 1974. This plan suited Dick Berry as it dispensed with pumping at Cloughs Cross. Known as the "Bowyer" scheme, cost was estimated at £996,046 including 5% consulting fees, Clark's scheme had been estimated at £940,000 for main-river works.

These figures only related to the improvements to the arterial channels to the pumps and construction of the stations: many hundreds of miles of District drains needed improvement to take full advantage of the new pumping scheme.

Stage I, consisting of Newborough, Postland, and Padholme catchments, commenced in October, 1972, on the Main River and contracts were let for the three pumping stations together.

The Newborough station was sited by the Welland Bank at the old barrow pit at the end of Wrights Drove, where Farran had recommended pumping in 1939, and Postland near Cloot House, Crowland: each was to be fed by completely new channels reversing the existing flow, Newborough 2.58 miles, Postland 2.65 miles and Padholme 1.25 miles. Land was purchased for the new Main River channels, plus 15 ft either side for permanent machine access and compensation paid for spoil coverage. The spoil would end up a long flat slope to allow cultivation, the topsoil being stripped over the whole area and replaced when the spoil bank profile was completed. This operation required considerable earth-moving in view of the huge quantities being excavated. Newborough 182,000 cubic metres and Postland 107,000 cubic metres.

I had detailed and protracted negotiations with Alan Ashpole, the County Council Land Agent, whose Council owned most of the land on the channel route in Newborough: sometimes he appeared to be negotiating for a trunk road, not a scheme to benefit their land-holding. It was eventually necessary to mention the River Board powers. However, everything was settled reasonably amicably, considering he was an appointed member of the new IDB.

A similar situation arose in Postland with the Crown Commissioners, regarding gravel land near Crowland on Mr Butcher's tenancy. They settled for giving the land required, free of cost, but all the gravel excavated must be used for new access tracks alongside the drain, so they retained the freehold. Again, everything was settled amicably even with Mr Butcher, probably by direction of the Commissioners.

Much of the material excavated in Newborough was soft wet Blue Clay, so we had to keep some water in the excavation to get the material out of the large excavator buckets: it stuck fast and needed spreading out to dry before it could be handled to shape it into an embankment. The large "Pennines" with 80' Jibs had to work on mats. We also had to go through the prehistoric River Nene, Rodden, which Dick Berry and the ad hoc committee, maintaining a watching brief on the scheme, said would beat us. It was known as running silt: however, by pumping and taking a little at a time from the bed, we eventually achieved the correct channel section, or rather, an enlarged channel section, its original not being designed to the new criteria, Dick was aware of the slight increase in size. We also came across a "Wild Bore", an artesian overflow from the acquifiers, which ran a 9" pipe full during excavation, causing excessive pumping. It dried up during the drought year, 1976.

Another frustration was the lack of progress of the Pumping Station Contract when it became obvious that the contractors were going broke. I suggested to Peter Langford, now the engineer, Geoff having moved to AWA, that the contract should be stopped, but he wouldn't concur. I stopped the contract myself on the grounds that the cofferdam was unsafe, calling in the factory inspector who agreed. The next contractors were totally different, but we had lost time. Postland had proceeded much more according to plan, by September, 1973, we were nearing completion, then faced further frustration. Dick Berry and T R Pick, (Chairman of the River Authority), decided to open the pumping station on 26th September, the occasion of T R Pick's last inspection, (the Anglian Water Authority were taking over), and I had to arrange the Fen element of the inspection.

Openings of Land Drainage Pumping Stations are traditionally great events: happening only every 30/40 years, and very grand, with plaques, (with curtains), champagne and nibbles, speeches patting everyone on the back, the "drawing of the curtains", with the ceremonial starting of the pumps. Everything must be shining bright, nothing out of place. Even the workmen had new overalls.

This occasion had to be special, so I arranged for two stone barges to be on the River Welland, duly painted, and covered with wooden framework supporting a polythene cover in case of inclement weather. They were to proceed a couple of miles down-stream where a new pump at the Welland and Deeping pumping station was to be started, then to a roadway on the other side of the river, for the guests to disembark into coaches for transport to T.R. Pick's house for lunch in a marquee.

At 6 am on the 25th, it was bedlam on site. Grass hadn't grown on the embankment so it needed turfing. The Electricity Board did the final connections. Contractors were putting up handrails and painting the Control Building. Lorries delivered gravel to be spread on the access area and an excavator was cleaning up the river bank. The driver, deciding to help the gravel-spreading in front of the barges, tracked over the bank and missed his travelling gear. Down the machine trundled, straight over the edge, the Jib landing across the barges with an almighty crash, the barge stopping the machine from going in the river. By 11 am next morning, everything was pristine; after a late night and several beers.

It was a great day, good weather, organisation and food, marred only by my being instructed to look after one speaker who over-imbibed later, and when everybody had gone was left behind asleep. No-one could wake or move him so we just left him. When he woke later, the Clerk had to take him home; He was not amused and I was on the carpet, but at least we were thanked by T R Pick!!

The North Level improvements beyond Main River commenced in Newborough on 10th September, in Postland on the 11th, with the same method of excavation, using all their plant together with hired machines.

We had, by now, perfected the use of 'ARMCO" multi-plate arches for road culverts, culminating in the installation of a large culvert on the Crowland-Spalding road which was installed in one piece, the road being closed for 24 hours only, a considerable achievement, especially as it was done without any shoring to the excavation.

By early 1974, the IDB had completed their length of main drain improvement and we started pumping, only to have problems with the pump-controls and syphons. Prior to letting of the pump contracts, I had pointed out that the tenders were not like for like, as the designers had failed to specify the TIP SPEEDS of the pump impellers; the firm selected were, in my opinion, quoting far too high tip speeds for pumping drainage water which contained all elements of suspended matter. The firm had no experience of land drainage pumping. Later I was proved right.

The Newborough Pumping Station was officially opened on 7th May, 1974, and the channel work on both schemes was complete so there was ample storage for pumping. It was a conscious and applaudable decision of the new IDB that the areas with the highest priority for improvement were Postland and Newborough, so with the completion of the pumping stations the Board vigorously began the improvement of District Main Drains.

After being the poor relation in the North Level for so long, Newborough became number one priority. Their rate-payers were to become the first beneficiaries of the 4th Major Improvement. By early 1975, the IDB had commenced five back-up schemes in Newborough.

It had been intimated that grants were available for Agricultural Development, (FEOGA), from the EEC, but on enquiry,our Ministry declared that any grants obtained by the Water Authority would be taken off main River Grants and that IDB's were not eligible.

In July, the Board's engineer, whose health was failing, retired and Dick Berry offered me the job! To my delight, I was appointed and joined the Board on 1st August, 1975.

We had started work on Cross Guns pumping station, the largest station to be constructed in the Fens since the war, under the capable direction of Geoff Beall, who had succeeded to my job. Had I stayed with the AWA, I would have been either promoted or sacked, probably the latter, knowing the new incumbent in Oundle, who had no drainage experience whatsoever. Those frustrating two years led me to ask how the long time chief of the Wisbech and District Water Company, Cyril Lanwarne, was coping with all the paper? "Great," he said, "We're running the central heating on it!" Things declined so much that the second year's Annual Report failed to mention Land Drainage and Sea Defence, these matters being included in "Other Activities". I was glad to be out of it.

The opportunity to continue a major improvement of this magnitude only occurs once in a Drainage Engineer's lifetime. Working with that financial genius, Roy Wedley, the Clerk and Financial Officer, was an added benefit; we made a formidable team. He often braked my enthusiasm, but always backed me. They were heady years.

Our first job was to programme the overall scheme. Dick insisted on a ten year plan, "No pussy footing about," he said, and persuaded the Board to finance the scheme on ten year period loans as required. All parts of the Board's area were to receive the same benefit of pumping.

The Murrow and Guyhirn areas of Northside were low and badly drained, and it had been proposed by WNRA to culvert the railway and include it in Cross Guns. The state of the railway and the Railway Company conditions so financially inflated the proposals that we sought an alternative, deciding to take the area Northwards to the New Wryde and making provision for pumping at Murrow. The area was at that time pumped to Mouth Lane in Wisbech Northside and Folley Drove. The scheme was adopted, thereby reducing the Northside pumped catchment.

The Ministry again intimated that we would be unlikely to qualify for FEOGA Grant, but added, if we were successful they would consider it a windfall, it would not affect the grant. Over the next few months, Roy badgered Brussels until we got to the right man, even persuaded the Board we should go to Brussels. We sent the Eurocrat all details, including cost benefit, and in 1976, Brussels approved a substantial grant. The Ministry were flabbergasted. This grant for the Murrow Scheme was the first of many: we finished with roughly 20% grant for IDB works for the rest of the overall scheme, this on top of the Ministry's 50% grant.

Cross Guns Pumping Station proceeded apace. So large was the station that it had to be built in two halves by the W.A. direct labour under the able direction of Terry Hill, promoted to construction foreman. I asked him to join the North Level, but we could not pay him enough!

The past policy of only hand improvements to the drains in Newborough was showing its inadequacies: to get improvement in bed levels many drains had to be widened 5 to 6 feet on either bank to achieve a $1.^1/_2$:1 bank slope, (batter), which would be stable. Huge amounts of spoil resulted which had to be spread to a depth of 4", compensation being paid for land lost and area covered by spoil, so the cost per metre for improvement of drains was twice as expensive as other areas which were maintained mechanically.

Whilst the IDB works were concentrated in Newborough, we dealt with a long-standing problem area at Kingston Hall, Throckenholt. This area had to drain along a tortuous route to Straight Reach with the South Eau only 200 metres away. The 4th District and the North Level Commissioners had constantly refused a connection, old parochiality again. A new Armco culvert was constructed under the bank and a new channel out to the South Eau with improvement of drains upstream giving free board to underdrainage. The landowners were delighted - one had pressed for improvements for 40 years.

At this time, the main drain from Tydd Gote to Parson Drove was an excellent coarse fishery, used by all and sundry, especially the big clubs from Yorkshire and the Midlands, for nothing! They had to make their own "arrangements" with the Board's bank tenants. We had no way of controlling litter and bank damage. The Tydd Angling Club was in operation, so I offered the Fishery to them at a reasonable sum with permission to let for matches, provided rubbish was cleared and bank damage controlled: all this was legally framed. Some years before I had considerable difficulty monitoring some of the large Northern Clubs. The River Board sold the fishing rights on the Nene, precluding the Oundle Fishing Club, which had had permission to fish the river by the town since the 18th Century, as they could not afford to compete with the big boys. After this letting, when the big boys found they now had to pay for their fishing, Roy received abusive letters and phone calls, including some threatening ones. The National Angling Executive, supported by the Annual Meeting, put an embargo on any club using the waters, the national press took this up with questions about competitive tendering, but were 'shot down' admirably by Roy Wedley. I knew the editor of the Angling Times, who ran a vitriolic attack on the big clubs. There followed a climb-down with suitable apologies, but the ban stayed. However, one of their own members ignored the ban and continued to fish matches. The Tydd Gote Club did some superb job "policing" and there was no trouble, a successful operation, followed by others in the area, resulting in increased income with no maintenance expenditure.

I was amazed that the Board had no plant replacement policy or fund; plant being brought from revenue, operating and running cost also being charged to that account. The new Board had an old 24 RB, old 22RB, two new 22 RB's, (bought on the Major scheme), Priestman Mustang hydraulic and three 10 RB's, together with vans, tractors, etc. The Board started the fund with £10,000 and all plant was charged to schemes at 10% less than the current hire rates. This system meant that, including "FEOGA", some 70% of the running costs and capital depreciation was paid for out of grant.

We also introduced a scale of charges for surface water from developments as a contribution toward increased flow and therefore pumping. There were no gravity outlets from the whole 97,000 acres to tidal waters: it had to be pumped. Surface water from development discharging into drains during heavy summer storms required pumping, whereas the flow from agricultural areas at this time of year was mostly absorbed.

1976 was a drought year, the driest for 250 years, when rain fell on the 1st August, the soil moisture deficit was at 141.3 mm. This is the amount of rain required to bring the soil to field capacity, ie saturation.

In the Fens, there is mention of the sock-level or the water-table level; this is the level where standing water is found and varies throughout the year. Many farmers and laymen believe that this water-level relates to the water-level in the drain. Generally speaking, this drain level will only affect the sock-level 10 to 15 ft from the drain - the sock-level in the field is entirely dependent on rainfall, evaporation and transpiration. As the sock goes down roots will follow, getting moisture from the soil particles mixed with air to produce capillary action. Roots do not penetrate further than the standing water.

During this dry year I demonstrated the above to the members with the co-operation of a local farmer. There were two twenty-acre potato fields, one where water had been kept 12 inches from ground level in the drain, while the other was dry. When the crop was off we dug a 16 foot deep hole in the centre of each field: in neither could we find standing water. In this year, January to August, there was 5" of rain from August to September 18". Nature usually recovers.

The water boreholes near Peterborough became affected by salt from the sea, at one stage water was flowing into the gravel bed on the South Eau, from upstream and downstream. Efforts ensued to transfer water from the Nene to the Welland which had dried up. This utilised the Thorney River and Bukehorne into Newborough and pumped into the Welland. When the system was partially running, it rained.

However, the good weather enabled construction to forge ahead at Cross Guns. Surveys were done and by early 1977 Mouth Lane was commenced with 1483 acres directed to Highside Drain, thence to the South Eau. Murrow was now operating by gravity into the New Wryde, the reduced agricultural flow to the new pumps being taken up by increased development flow. Drains were still being improved in the Newborough, one or two in Postland; however, the ground level was higher here and the main drain sections good, being mechanically maintained.

A new large gas main was commenced in 1977, passing through the Board's eastern area. This gave us valuable knowledge of subsoils, as we demanded boreholes at each ditch and drain crossing. With our updated survey we could insist on pipe levels adequate for all future drain improvements. I also negotiated a single payment of £5000 toward our pumping costs during construction.

The boreholes showed that most drains affected by "running silt" problems were where the silt was sitting on impervious blue clay at, or just below, the bed of the drain, so by slowly pumping out the surplus water in the silt during excavation we made the banks stable, even on drains which our members thought could not be drained without piling. The exceptions were on deep "Roddens".

Winter 1977/78 was very wet and many bank slips occurred on new drains excavated in clay, including a large slip in the main drain: it was a circular slip, the bed rising like a "stranded whale", caused by water from land behind percolating through cracks in the clay still there after the drought year. However, it was dealt with by the Board's staff efficiently.

In late 1976, the Government instituted Capital Expenditure Restriction on Water Authorities, possibly delaying Cross Guns and Mouth Lane Pumping Station construction and the supply of pumping plant. To keep the WA construction staff going, the Board decided to accelerate the programme for the IDB pumping stations at Denhams, Poplars and Willow Holt, the WA contracting to build them. Poplars was commenced in 1977, Denhams and Willow Holt, early 1978. Another reason for acceleration was the rumour that "FEOGA" grants might be removed by the Common Market.

There was feverish activity by WA engineers and our staff in 1977, preparing these schemes to send to our Ministry and the "FEOGA" people. Urgent works approval was given to enable us to start work and the schemes were accepted by "FEOGA", (once in the pipeline a grant could not be refused!). The Ministry controlled capital expenditure in IDB's by delaying approval for grants. However, through persuasion and co-operation we escaped any actual restrictions. Ours was the only major scheme underway in the country. The Ministry required a three-year programme of capital schemes from Boards, but we submitted a detailed five-year programme: maybe being positive helped.

In January 1978, there was almost a repeat of the meteorological condition of 1953, only this time the force 9 wind moved round to the N.E., blowing straight into the Wash. The East Coast Tide Warning system was in operation so a surge was predicted. However, this did not cater for the local effect in the Wash with the wind in this direction. The morning tide on the 11th January failed to ebb, remaining about two metres above predicted low water. There were four foot high waves at Sutton Bridge.

Some years previously, I had, on several occasions, alerted the Water Authority to the low areas of tidal defences around the docks and on the opposite bank, also an area along Cromwell Road bank in Wisbech, but this had been ignored. These areas had been omitted from the increased protection provided after 1953 on grounds of expense. The protection should have been at a level of 6'.10m., but was much lower in 1976, with a surge level of 4.99m. the water came over the bank at the turning bay. The 1953 surge level in Wisbech was 5.26m. and in 1978 it was 5.60m. with considerable wave action. Houses in North End, Wisbech in the North Level area and several roads were flooded as water came up surface drains to the river; water also penetrated through the North Brink Bank. 700 houses and 100 industrial and business properties were flooded with one fatality.

At the North Level outfall at Foul Anchor, the water got through the old outfall, which had to be refilled, and Buckworths sluice, (thought to have been demolished), blew out as clean as a whistle, the sluice arch in perfect condition: this flooded a small area and some properties.

Knowing that the diesel engines at Tydd were obsolete, I had been negotiating with Crossleys to take spares for the KO4 Engines. We sent them a list and arranged to inspect on the Monday, only to be

Bishoplands Drain Improvement - The Boards 22RB Excavators

told early in the morning that their stores had burnt down over the weekend and all spares were useless.

Back-up schemes on the Board's drains were proceeding apace, with improvements in Tydd and Northside underway. We followed up with hydraulic seeding, a method of blowing selected grass seed, complete with a compost mixture and an adhesive agent, on the batters. Initial germination took place in the mulch and quickly rooted. This prevented batter erosion on friable soils due to run off from the land in heavy summer storms. On some larger batters we sprayed bitumen emulsion on top of the seed mixture, which was successful. Again, we piped all side ditches to give continual mechanical maintenance on both banks.

With all this activity in progress, there was a summer flood: 2.73" of rain fell in three days in May, 1978, producing immediate run-off. The ground was still cracked after the drought year and the water went down the cracks into the drain. A jet of water poured from a crack 2 metres down the batter, taking us all by surprise. We had to do emergency works at Poplars to connect to the gravity outlet, then install a 12" pump as the Main Drain suddenly rose. The existing pumping station in Northside was still operating, also the three electric pumps at Cross Guns were operable. Newborough, Postland and Padholme coped adequately and land drains were not covered. Five engines functioned for 19 hours non-stop at Tydd, except for 6 hours when the weedscreen blocked with rubbish. It took a JCB, tractor and trailer and eight men to clear it. Towards the end of this period, pump No. 4 bearings failed and the engine was stopped, but we had broken the back of the flood. We also found time to renew the old iron access bridges, built as part of the 1832 major scheme with Bailey bridges, as part of the current major scheme.

By December, 1978, Mouth Lane Pumping Station was operating and Cross Guns Pumping Station had been opened in September. We were progressing with the construction of Denhams and Poplar and the back-up drain works. Before this, we had negotiated a contract with ARMCO Ltd. to supply corrugated steel pipes and pipe-arches for the major scheme, resulting in 15% reduction in list price. We took delivery of full lorry loads of pipes, but pipe arches were delivered to site as they needed craneage to off-load. For large road culverts, these were semi-elliptical with a flat invert to conform with the bed width with sloping ends: the blokes became so skilled that once they had been bolted up we could put them in within 12 hours, and not a lump of concrete in sight.

Fen engineers having been very sceptical about the present state of art for Fenland channel design, I suggested to the Ministry that Newborough would be an ideal area for a hydrological research programme, involving both Institute of Hydrology and the Hydraulic Research Institute. Level-recorders and a rainfall station area were installed and flow-monitoring commenced to check pump discharges. This was the start of a major research project involving the North Level.

Mouth Lane pumping station was officially opened on 14th September, 1979, with most of the drain works completed. Immediately afterwards construction began of Willow Holt pumping station and a contract proposed for the drain works. We were at full stretch. Somewhat reluctantly, the Board agreed to radio-telephones being installed. If you haven't got these communication tools, you could do with them, once you have them, you wonder how you managed without them. They proved an absolute godsend, producing a speedy reaction-time to problems or complaints.

In 1979, the Water Authority had started raising the sea banks and nearly all the spoil on the back-up schemes in the Tydd and Gorefield area was carted away at no expense to the Board except restoration. This reduced the cost of these schemes considerably. They also removed the old spoil banks on the main drain at Tydd pumping station.

The drain improvement in Newborough and Padholme completed, concern was expressed by the owners of the area where peat was overlying dense gravel and sand, that the lower drainage-levels were denuding their land of moisture. I produced a paper for the members describing the effect of the scheme on water-table levels, Newborough members were not convinced, we were asked to produce a pilot summer water-retention scheme using temporary dams. New water-retaining structures were put in Padholme upstream of the main pumping channel. This small area had been subjected to a Cambridge University subsoil study some years previously which concluded that the subsoil was porous enough to benefit from underground irrigation through it in the summer, but the Newborough subsoil was considerably denser. A further benefit to Newborough was that it was served by two freshwater inlets from the Folly River and the Welland, legacies of the cattle days.

These temporary dams were placed in Newborough for two summer periods, gratifying the complaining landowners. They, however, saw the possibility of utilising the penned water for irrigation from the freshwater intakes. I advised the Board to resist this, as the temporary dams could not be removed easily during a summer inundation and they would be liable if land flooded. They agreed.

*The Old Northside Rummers Pumping Station - now a private house.
The site of Six Great Wind Engines.*

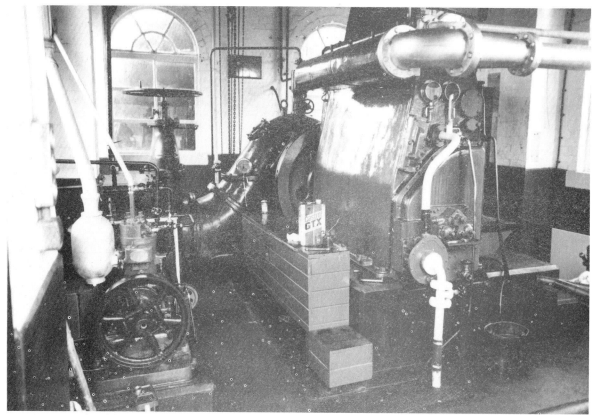

The Old Northside Pumping Station at Mouth Lane, installed in 1936 - still in working order.

The New Cross Guns Pumping Station

*The Old French Drove Boost
Pumping Station*

Peakirk Pumping Station

Dehams Pumping Station

Hundreds Pumping Station

Postland Pumping Station

Newborough Pumping Station

Poplars Pumping Station

Willow Holt Pumping Station

*Mouth Lane
New Pumping Station*

Tidal Floods - 1978

CHAPTER XIII

Into the Fully Automated Eighties

When the North Level IDB was formed in 1973, we employed 79 men, by 1980, numbers declined as the "old boys" retired; we no longer employed men over 65, there were fewer skilled scythe men and we had already moved towards mechanical operations. By now we had many side dykes piped giving continual access. Concerned about summer flooding, the Board decided to pay compensation for going through growing crops.

There was now a new "River Man" with the Water Authority, David Noble. He, the engineers of the two neighbouring Boards, and I, held regular meetings culminating in all three Boards, with the River Division, commissioning the Agricultural College at Silsoe to carry out a drain-survey of the three areas and produce ideas for a completely new, purpose designed weedcutting machine which would operate from within drains. The drain survey proved valuable in the future.

1979 was an exceptionally wet year. 7.49" of rain fell in three Spring months, testing low pumped areas which took the run-off in their stride, but areas yet to be completed had land drains under water over 24 hours. The results of monitoring of Newborough were revised design criteria and vindicated my decision to enlarge the main drains. This rainfall caused problems with back-up schemes occasioning considerable pumping of excavations which helped some areas, but created difficulties at the new pumping station sites.

8" of snow fell in December, with heavy frosts producing thick ice on the drains. Considerable drifting occurred and many drains, including the Main Drain, were filled up. All available staff broke ice at the pumping stations. Fortunately, the thaw was slow with only light rain, nevertheless considerable pumping was required. The annual pumping hours between April, 1979, and March, 1980, were 10,616 compared with an estimated 5,053. This completely over loaded the pumping budget and was one reason the Board tried to retain "balances" in order to avoid "peaks and troughs" in the rates.

By early 1980, Denhams and Poplars pumping Stations became operable. At Cross Guns we were having problems with the diesel pump, mostly with the gear boxes. Willow Holt was progressing and the drain works had been let to contract. Dog in a Doublet was in progress, using the Board's 22RB rigged as a crane and drain works had commenced. There was another wet period in February and March, 1980, with 4,637 pumping hours recorded. The new pumping scheme was working, but pumping costs were rising as new stations came on line.

The problems associated with unmanned automatic pumping stations were now coming to light, so high and low water sensors were installed together, and sensors indicating syphon operations connected to the telephone. On activation, a member of the pumping station staff was called out. These amendments were accepted for grant and applied to new stations, the costs were recovered by 1981. Many faults occurred at Newborough and Postland pumping stations, for which we had been operationally responsible from the AWA in early 1980. The system was labour consuming, and sparked an idea in my mind.

The final report from Silsoe was received, including proposals for the construction of a machine and a survey of continental machines already existing, with the comment that none were suitable for our mechanical weedcutting operations. The consortium Committee of Board Members and Engineers, looking after the "Mechanical Plant Project", as the commission was now called, disagreed and instructed the engineers to examine thoroughly the available plant. This hectic five day trip, organised by Joe Price, brought a recommendation to the Boards to further investigate several useful pieces of plant which would be suitable for weedcutting operations. The recommended plant was manufactured in Germany and Holland and operated there. We met the development engineers who produced the prototypes originally, as agricultural engineers and contractors, by demand from Drainage Authorities and farmers: as their machines were successful, they had expanded into manufacturing.

Virtually no Drainage Authorities in these countries carried out improvements with their own staff: it was all done by contract, often by a single farmer/contractor in a Drainage Authority area, a contract monopoly based on trust! This was fertile ground for producing labour-saving plant. Two pieces of plant caught our eye: the bicycle and the spider.

Newborough Village was destined for expansion under the District plan: surface drainage was abysmal and development would produce flooding. With the co-operation of the District Council the Board agreed to an improvement scheme, half agricultural and half development grant aided.

The owner of 150 acres of grassland, severed from Newborough by the cutting of the Folly River in the 18th Century, bounded in the west by the old Car Dyke and drained into Newborough by a culvert under the river, requested improvement in order to underdrain and turn it into arable. Much of this land had been the subject of the lawsuit due to flooding, which the Newborough Drainage Commission lost.

At the outset of the Major Scheme, the Board had resolved that all land in the North Level would be drained to the same standard, therefore this small area was no exception. We installed a Small submersible pump in a chamber which pumped into the Folly River and cut a short main drain: the farmer did the rest and eventually underdrained the area. He also undertook to look after the pump, a successful enterprise completed in October, 1980.

At this time, we had a horrific accident with our machine at the Dog in the Doublet. The machine had tracked a short distance along the road with its jib flat to avoid the overhead wire and with the bucket strapped to it. The driver turned off the road to go down the slope to the pumping station site, missed his travelling gear, and the machine headed down the slope toward the White Swan. The Board had sold the pub in 1976, it was now a private house. There was no way of stopping the twenty-two ton machine and to the driver's dismay, the jib head went straight through the dormer window and emerged from the roof at the back before the machine came to rest. The lady of the house rushed out, white-faced, but calmly commented, "Thank God your uninvited entry was not earlier, a minute ago I was sitting on the loo." The shocked driver did not recognize the significance of the remark. Arriving ten minutes later however, I did - the large excavator bucket was sitting squarely on the toilet seat!

There was surprisingly little damage to the house, but considerably more after we had removed the machine, mainly caused by the bucket, but we made the house weatherproof with tarpaulins. I remember a neat notice board by the machine tracks reading PLEASE KEEP OFF THE GRASS!

1981 brought a major test of the pumping system already installed, when between January and April 10.67" of rain fell, 3.93" in March, and the design run-off of 20 acres/100 acres was achieved. Further rainfall in April meant the May pumping hours were 713.$^1/_4$ compared to 170 for the similar period in 1980. All completed areas reached their maximum design-flow and no land drains were underwater. In other areas, land drains went under water for long stretches: Willow Holt and Mouth Lane were both beaten for about two hours - the ground still had not fully recovered from the drying out after the drought year of 1976. Cracks in the clay subsoil were still open: this was good for drainage, but produced an immediate run-off. This event vindicated my decision to increase design criteria from the Clark 1969 report. Newborough worked well with the pumps operating although the bank growth was by now established.

The sewage counter drain, taking effluent from Peterborough sewage works to the Peterborough Sewage Pumping Station at the Dog in a Doublet, was completely overloaded and flooding occurred. The emergency overflow to the North Level pumps operated for 39 hours, which affected the Dog in a Doublet catchment; water was also diverted to Cross Guns when water levels in that area dropped. The Water Authority agreed to improve the drain and install new pumps.

We now produced a comprehensive report for the Board on the Mechanical Maintenance of Drains, categorising drains and their maintenance standards, (the Silsoe report being very useful), and recommending plant requirements on the basis of keeping the main drains clear for summer floods. The Welland and Deeping Board bought a conver "Bicycle" tractor and the South Holland a Berkenbegar "Spider" which appeared to be operating successfully. The Board agreed my proposals and purchased a "Spider" in 1982. We were now down to 35 men.

In December that year, (1981), we had severe frosts with 3"-5" of ice on all drains, much to the delight of the skaters, but a nightmare to Drainage Authorities. All available staff were used to keep the weedscreens free from ice. At Postland and Newborough, the syphon valve heaters proved totally inadequate in their exposed positions, the telephone alarms failed to operate and telephone lines were down. Both pumping stations syphoned the River back with all pumps operating for 12 hours and Newborough ran dry, due to ice in the air control tube. This cost the Board £6,000 in wasted electricity and the fault was only found by Arthur Atkins, who had trouble at the other stations. This was when the automation idea began to grow in my mind.

June, 1982, there was another summer flood. This showed the efficacy of mechanical and chemical maintenance and the ever present danger of summer rainfall. In 1905, there was 4.05", June, 1936, 4.05", 1958, 4.82" 1982, 4.78": the wet summer caused problems for the AWA who were still carting away spoil for restoration of the tidal banks from our back-up scheme. In turn, we had to do more work on restoring the spoil areas.

I prepared a computerised monitoring and control plan for pumping, utilising our existing radio system, and wrote a specification for an eventual automated computer control structure. I was finally in a position to put my proposals to the Board, but how could I put a highly technical and sophisticated report in a form understandable to a layman? I kept altering my presentation to the Board, until at last the great day arrived.

All members had copies of my simplified report to read before the meeting. I proposed to take the Board into the 21st century. Such was my enthusiasm and keenness not to miss out anything that I spoke for twenty minutes without looking to see the reaction. Eventually, a note from the chairman in big red letters was thrust under my nose. It said, "SHUT UP, YOU'VE SOLD IT'. Startled, I glanced up. Some members were doodling, some talking, others dozing, most appeared totally bored. I was later told I went bright red, mumbled an apology and shut up like a clam. "What a bloody fool," I thought. The venerable, intelligent farmers had grasped the significance of my proposals and understood most of the details. The vote in favour was unanimous, with approval for the clarity of my presentation. It was the most satisfying and embarrassing day of my life. I had called the scheme "AFCOPS", Automatic Flood Control of Pumping Stations. From then, when my enthusiasms started me waffling, I received little notes with "AFCOPS" on. That happy day has caused much hilarity among the members, being often recounted. I certainly learned my lesson.

There was still a lot of work to do on AFCOPS before tenders could be prepared and the scheme submitted to the Ministry for grant, but the major scheme was still onward-going: Dog in a Doublet pumping station was nearing completion and the Tydd pumping station updating was underway, back-up schemes were still in 'full flow'.

At the end of 1982, we had 25.47" of rainfall compared to the 30 year average of 22.35".

Land drainage engineers then appreciated the advantages of hydraulic machines over the dragline, with the ability of positive dig at full reach, and to lift out that dig without dragging like a dragline, and were demanding ever longer reaches. This demand was producing heavier machines with massive balance weights to counter-balance the weight of the jibs and pay-load. Priestman had a theory, and asked several engineers, including me, if they would co-operate in assessing ideas. The result was the VC15, which had a light weight two piece jib, a good payload and a reach of 45 ft, suitable for maintenance of most main drains, with a moveable balance weight. As the jib went out, the balance weight moved back and vice versa: weight was kept to a minimum, a brilliant concept. The first machine was demonstrated at Tydd Gote in early 1983, and we bought it with a discount and a further 10.46% discount for Engineer Development Assistance; it gave many years' sterling service and was followed by even larger machines with longer reaches.

In 1982, we had decided that French Drove pumping station was a white elephant, so we set about improving Morris Fen to discharge upstream of this structure. The channel was designed to take a pumping station, pumping into the South Eau, similar to the Murrow Scheme, which had worked well since 1974 without pumping. We were looking ahead twenty years at least. The Morris Fen Scheme was completed in 1985, and to date has proved successful without pumping.

The Dog in a Doublet came on line early 1983, so there was now only the main installation left to complete the major scheme, the updating of Tydd Pumping Station and main channel works and the Hundreds Drain area of Newborough, although the back-up schemes still had some way to go.

The Board had nearly reached their original target of completion in ten years, when thwarted by capital investment restrictions applied by the Ministry of Agriculture to the Water Authority and their

The Revolutionary Priestman V.C.15 with sliding balance weight

The Great Dick Berry

*Dog in a Doublet Pumping
Station showing
soundproof cabinets*

The Opening of Dog in a Doublet Pumping Station

own land drainage restrictions. The roles were reversed at Tydd, the North Level becoming consultants to the Water Authority as well as contractors. The Board made the irrevocable decision that gravity discharge to tidal waters was no longer possible and in future the whole 79,000 acres had to be pumped, two thirds of the area twice.

In view of the age of diesel engines we decided to install a new electric pump, envisaged in the Bowyer report, also to electrify two of the diesel pumps, these three electrics carrying out most of the duty pumping, with three diesels on standby or used during major pumping events. The old Protection Sluice was completely blocked, also the openings under the pumping station, the old gravity flow channels. A negotiated contract was let with Allen Gwynnes of Bedford for the electrification of the diesels, (they were the original suppliers), and the new pump went to tender, Gwynnes being successful, all this work was soon going ahead.

In early 1983, Dick Berry became ill and retired as chairman at the Annual General Meeting, although he continued as a member of the Board for some years, (I believe he regretted giving up the chair as his health subsequently improved). David Coates succeeded him, not as rugged as Dick, but his gentlemanly approach won approval, a great smoother of waves was David and a highly supportive chairman to Roy and me.

Fortunately, Dick was in office long enough for the Board to give him the honour of officially opening the Dog in a Doublet pumping station. Making speeches was not Dick's forte, but he was magnificent that day, amidst a lot of emotion and champagne. It was a day to remember, he was a wonderful chap.

This was a year of extreme activity. With the help of David Noble, AWA, we had got Main River Grant on AFCOPS, now estimated at £92,000 and work was well on, but not without difficulties: we learnt as we went along. We were experiencing trouble with sensors as well as the computer side. Again, there was heavy rainfall in April and May, during which pump Nº 5 at Tydd failed.

When Arthur Atkins and crew stripped down the 48" pump, they found that the sleeve on the tail end of the shaft had unscrewed and the steel shaft had been running in the sleeve instead of the sleeve running in the bearing: this could only have happened if the pump had run backward, but there was no record. Fortunately, Eric Elam, the pump man in 1939, who was still living, admitted that the engine had run backward when he lost his gate-valve turning, but only for a few moments. So the shaft had been running in the sleeve since 1939. British workmanship indeed, they were built to last in those days.

Alan Gwynnes, the pump manufacturer, said the shaft and impeller had to go back to the works for turning down and fitting a new sleeve, and new bearing shells, about £4000 worth. They would send their most experienced fitter to put it back. About £800 of shells were delivered after four weeks, but Arthur discovered the grease-holes were wrong, so back they went. On return, the fitter asked Arthur for an angle-grinder to shave off part of the casting because they didn't fit. "Not bloody likely," said Arthur, and packed him off complete with shells. He then stripped down French Drove pump, (they were similar pumps), checked the sleeves, shafts and impeller, which had little wear, and installed them at Tydd, using the old shells. He ran the pump for a few hours, did some 'wiping' to the shells and it was serviceable. It is still running today. The shaft and impeller returned from Gwynnes, suitably weather-proofed, are on view at the station today. The bill was a lot less!

Before this event, Arthur and his merry men had taken nine months to redecorate the station, engines and pumps: Dick Berry was flabbergasted, having honestly believed that the engines were originally painted black, not traditional pump green. All the oil leaks had been stopped and it was quite a picture. The pride the chaps had in their station was a joy, their slogan; 'No fags on the floor please, don't handle the bright work!'

Talking to Eric Elam, I discovered the reason for not running the pumps at design revs. They were old and rattled badly at full revs, Eric grinned, adding that five pumps running at lower revs were easier on the ears during a night watch! After that, they ran at full revs - when I was there.

In 1981, I had taken over from Des Miles as secretary to the Technical Committee of ADA, (The Association of Drainage Authorities). The committee decided to produce a quarterly magazine intending it to be self-supporting. David Noble, (now Hon. Sec. of the ADA), and I had many midnight oil burning sessions until the first issue appeared in Autumn 1983. Initially produced by a chap in Boston, David took over because of a host of errors, misprints, failure of distribution plus an element of rip-off. It has since been successful.

We clashed with the conservationists later in the year, even hitting the national press and television. The pound banks downstream of Tydd apparently supported a native orchid, called Autumn Ladies Tresses, so the tenants agreed a grazing policy and not to use sprays. This had gone on since the seventies, but a lady in the village found some of these orchids upstream of the pumping station on the length to be improved. She promptly telephoned the national press, accusing us of destroying the plants, this being their northern limit of growth. The 'phone buzzed with reporters, Naturalist Trusts, Nature Conservation - you name it we got it. I stated the facts and the Board's position, then refused any interviews until Nature Conservancy replied exonerating the Board and their actions. We finally moved 30 plants to the already recognized area. All the naturalists confirmed that this was the most northern limit of growth which made the plant special; since when they have been discovered on the Welland Banks, and as far north as the Humber! No wonder I am sceptical of dogmatic statements issued by conservationists, amateur and professional. I recall how, after some years of badgering, I finally got scientists in the Nature Conservancy and the Institute of Terrestrial Studies to recognise that there had been NO wetlands in the Fens since the 19th century, but there were many areas of high-water-level grazing and a multitude of true wetlands in the uplands of Great Britain.

A further step to automation came when the Ministry of Agriculture agreed to finance a study by the Institute of Hydrology for the production of new design criteria for Fenland Drainage based on Newborough catchment.

Not a day passed without something new arising. A board member whose house was some two hundred yards away from the new Dog in a Doublet pumps and behind a bank, asked me to go there when the pumps were working. Outside his house, I heard a high-pitched whine, louder than near the pumps, but not uncomfortably so. Indoors, he gave me a large whisky and said, "Sit there for a few minutes." We chatted a while, then suddenly his collection of cut glasses in a glass-fronted cabinet sprang to life, rattling, clinking and singing so loudly we could hardly hear ourselves speak. We took some glasses out of the cabinet making sure none were touching, but there was no difference. When the sound consultant heard it, he was amazed, but managed to track down a wavelength against which the pump was finally shrouded. End of problem, some £1,200 later. This led to sound wavelength specifications for outside motors, adopted by the Ministry.

I suggested to the Board that pumping stations could not be considered wholly automatic unless supplied with automatic weedscreen cleaners. AFCOPS was already monitoring water-levels inside and outside the weedscreen in order to raise the alarm on blockage, involving labour which we were trying to reduce, so it was a logical progression. These cleaners were in common use in land drainage in Holland, so we went to inspect them. This resulted in the BOSKER cleaner being ordered for the Tydd pumping station.

Early in 1984, I recommended a complete scheme for mechanised maintenance. The Berkenheger spider was delivered, also a bicycle tractor flail cutter, further tractors with flail cutters and all machines were fitted with weedcutting buckets. Previously, we had increased the machine fuel capacity to last a full working week. These were supplied weekly by a fuel bowser. Other plant was similarly adapted; no longer were fuel barrels needed. All this was virtually financed from the Plant Replacement Fund and reduction in labour, without affecting the Board's rates, some maintenance still being performed by contract in peak times. The problems of summer flooding were solved.

Our design of the pumping scheme required that all pumped areas had a "back door" in case of electrical or pump failure. Newborough could discharge through Hundreds Drain to the South Eau, Postland to the Dowesdale arm , Denhams, Poplars and Willow Holt had gravity outlets to the Shire Drain and Main Drain, but Mouth Lane was out on a limb, so we decided to automate it to AFCOPS.

All the new pumps were syphon-assisted, meaning they pumped over a syphon above the tidal banks, so when the pump switched off, the water in the pipe ran back through the pump. On a diesel, of course, this made the engine run backwards for a few moments. The diesel engine manufacturers agreed that the engines would start on full load in gear. Arthur Atkins had tried stopping and starting the pump at various states of the tide, without adverse effects. There was a very high tide one Saturday morning. Arthur was not available, so I decided to try it, in order to be sure in my own mind. It worked OK with just one or two puffs from the engine. I left it for a while, then to simulate the stop/start normal operations of pumping, tried it again with a warm engine. One or two puffs, a few more, then more regularly, the station filled with exhaust fumes, the engine started taking off. The electric stop button was useless. Coughing and spluttering, I put the engine out of gear, of course, without load it went faster, so I smashed it into gear again and dashed outside. I could not breathe and expected the engine to blow up. I had seen an engine run backwards with disastrous results, but fortunately re-applying the load was enough to stop it.

When the smoke cleared I returned to have a look. What a mess. The station was covered in hang-

Weedcutting (Roding)

*Mechanical Weedcutting
with Hydraulic Excavator*

The Berkanhegar Weedcutting Machine - 'Spider'

The Berkanhegar 'Bycycle' Flail Cutting Machine

*The Thorney River lining and Conservation Scheme -
part of the Water Transfer arrangement from the Nene to the South Eau.*

ing globules of greasy soot. Everything was black. Arthur thought it was hilarious, despite two days of cleaning up. We put in a hydraulic piston to operate the gear level and the engine was successfully automated for remote starting on AFCOPS. Needless to say, the system was tested rigorously before being put on line. This automation was the completion of part one of AFCOPS.

Having completed the bulk of the major scheme and back-up works, many farmers in the area were considering the possibilities of irrigation out of the main drains and suggesting that the penning levels in the summer could be higher. The temporary damming scheme in Newborough had worked.

We prepared a Water Distribution scheme for the North Level western area, which the Board approved and decided to implement whether a grant was available or not. The scheme was not primarily designed to encourage irrigation, but to push the salt-water barrier further east and improve water quality to as big an area as possible and as far as the main drain. This would enhance flora and fauna in the system - good ecological stuff.

We sealed the Thorney River with steel piles along the porous bank and cleaned it out, feeding water into both the Dog in a Doublet and Cross Guns pumped areas, improved the top end of Thorney River to feed the Morris Fen area and Bukehorn, thence to the South Eau Main Drain. The temporary dams in Newborough were replaced with permanent Dam Board structures on Highland Drain feeding into the Hundreds Drain, thence into the South Eau. We put a new freshwater feed into South Drain from the Car Dyke and improved the other two.

By monitoring water-levels and pump-levels through AFCOPS, we found we could switch off pumps and allow water-levels to rise utilising the 'back door' from each pumping area as an overflow. The Board ruled that they were not to be involved in extra pumping costs to support irrigation, and abstraction would not be allowed to the detriment of water-users further downstream.

I proposed a new sluice in the Main Drain at Harold's Bridge to replace the one proposed at Cloughs Cross, which was being constructed when the 1968 flood occurred and never completed. However, many members remembered 1968 and decided to wait and see before going ahead.

The updating of Tydd pumping station progressed speedily, the electric pump was operating in early 1985, however, the outfall pipe failed and several months passed before this was rectified. This did not delay the electrification of one of the diesels which had its own particular problem of how to get the old engines out. The overhead crane was rated at about three tons and we knew that the fly-wheel and block weighed more. I had the crane re-tested and the new maximum load meant these parts could be hauled slowly and carefully without breaking them up. When I mentioned this to Tom Thrower, who worked as a carpenter on the station, I discovered that they had put in the pumps and engines first then erected the building. However, Arthur and his men managed.

Gwynnes had problems getting their new pump into the station, not having thought about how to do it. I suggested cutting a hole in the roof and they pay for the restoration. They put it in with a huge crane from outside the building and a new glazed skylight put in the roof improved the lighting.

The control system of the operation of the valves was a one-off, first in the world. Automated valves were usually made 'fail-safe' by using heavy balance weights which closed the valve, here we did not have sufficient headroom. Of two alternatives, hydraulics or air, I chose air as there were air-pipes, compressors and receivers already in the station. A battle of trial and error began, overseen by Arthur Atkins, who was not easily satisfied. He must have saved Gwynnes and the Board thousands of pounds by his practical suggestions.

I could write a saga on the updating of Tydd pumping station, but by early 1986, one electrical pump and the new pump were operating through AFCOPS and the Main River Improvement was nearly complete.

The second pump was electrified in 1986 with less trouble. The outfall pipe was satisfactorily repaired and all pumps were working by March, just in time to be tested by a major flood. The air-equipment and automatic controls were still giving problems and two pumps could not be used. Field capacity was reached in December, 1985, lasting until April. We had 4.01" of rain in March and April and estimated we pumped 44,260 million cubic metres and 21% of the rainfall ran off. After this pumping we decided, with Ministry approval, to strip down the remaining diesels to put them into as prime a condition as possible, a good job too, as one of them had cavitation in the impeller and shroud, duly repaired by Arthur and his men, aided by a specialist protection firm.

The weedscreen platform was widened, the weedscreen cleaner installed: the first in a land drainage pumping station in the Fens. It worked without failing, from its installation up to today, (1994). Construction work at this station was performed by the Board's staff, except final decorating, done by con-

The 'Charnley' Flail Cutting Machine from a painting by Les Pooly.
(The Dutch are now - 1994 - making a tracked 'Bycycle')

tract, because time was short.

The new mechanical weed clearance operation worked well. I had devised a tracked flail cutting machine to deal with most banks in one pass, only requiring a working strip of four feet. The Board agreed its development to a limit of £50,000 and I found an interested manufacturer. The cutting-heads were sensor-operated to a cutting height of 200 mm: it was unnecessary to cut closer. It was taking a while to develop, but market research was promising.

Stage II of AFCOPS was underway, the conversion of the monitoring-and-manual-control to computer control: later, in 1986, Newborough was successfully operated by computer!

My last view day was on my birthday, September 1986, when I was due to retire. We opened Tydd pumping station and celebrated. The Board gave me a great send off including the KISSOGRAM arranged by Roy and the rest of the guys and girls. I was a bit overcome during my speech, but managed to finish it.

This date signified the completion of the major scheme within thirteen years instead of the originally proposed ten, not bad, considering all the difficulties and restrictions. I was delighted that Dick Berry, the architect and drive of the whole scheme, was there to witness the culmination of his endeavours. The great man died suddenly in 1987.

Some ten days later, I embarked on another life-long ambition. I sailed the Atlantic in a 48' ketch and cruised around the West Indies for six months.

The Opening of the improved Tydd Pumping Station

The Opening of the improved Tydd Pumping Station.
L to R: My son, Simon, Les Pooley, Chairman David Coates

Tydd Pumping Station

Inside Tydd Pumping Station

Self & 'Friend' - Arthur Atkins looking 'pensive'

RETIREMENT: Land Drainage Style!

CHAPTER XIV

After Charnley

Rod Hunt and Steve Morris between them took over the engineering functions of the Board, with Roy as Wedley Chief Executive. The Board progressed at a more leisurely pace, gradually reducing the financial load as the ten years, loan dropped out. The major scheme cost eight and a quarter million pounds.

In 1985, we had developed a number system for all the Board's drains and produced a new map for the Members: this was preparation to computerising the Board's records, and came into its own when the Board joined the Drainage Board Computer Consortium, based at King's Lynn, in 1987.

In 1987, the estimated cost of the Tracked Flail cutter was £79,000 compared to the original approved £50,000, so the Board cancelled its development. These things happen.

At Cross Guns, the cylinder-liners in the Dorman engines were found to be porous after only ten years. I never liked high-speed diesels for land drainage work due to intermittent usage. At installation, the Ministry refused grant-aid for slow-running marine diesels, although most pumping station engines in Holland are marine diesels.

Before I retired, we had completed the River Improvement for the Hundreds Drain area without a pumping station, similar to Morris Fen and Murrow, but unlike those two, flood events showed land drains under water for long periods and water levels in the South Eau were affecting discharge. A new pumping station, incorporating a tilting gravity door, was started in 1987, completed in 1988. I still believe pumping stations will be required at Murrow and Morris Fen, but we were unable then to persuade the Ministry, although they insisted on the drain being lowered to take stations.

In 1987, AFCOPS again proved itself when the Electricity Boards abolished special Land Drainage Electricity Tariffs and introduced several bands of unit charges in 24 hours: the Board was able to change the pump-operating programme to take advantage of cheap rates at no extra cost.

Winter, 1987/88, was exceptionally wet, field capacity being reached in November and snow and rain in January produced 49.7 mm on a saturated catchment. All pumps worked at Tydd with 24 hour pumping on the diesels. Cross Guns used all pumps, again with 24 hour pumping on the diesels, all other pumps in the area worked flat out. Newborough worked on full computer control successfully. The 4th Major Improvement came through with flying colours, proving that Hundreds Drain needed pumping. Murrow and Morris Fen were on the limit. Resulting from this flood, Steve Morris persuaded the Ministry to finance further work by the Institute of Hydrology on the Postland and the Dog in a Doublet catchments, in order to confirm their revolutionary design criteria. The flood also confirmed the inadequacy of the Highside system, from Wisbech to the Main Drain, now the longest gravity system in the North Level area. I think that area will eventually need pumping.

By early 1989, AFCOPS was recording polling, monitoring with graphs and analysis for all stations, information being stored on floppy disk for future use, when operations will be fully computerised.

The excessive pumping showed up further problems at Postland and the remaining pumps had to be sent away for repairs, one at a time, each with the same problem of cavitation. Fortunately, the Ministry grant aided the repair, but by now it had dropped to 25%. The station was fully restored by early 1990.

The Board now embarked on a complete appraisal of the Highland system, including proposed development in order to establish the future load. The system was fully surveyed and a report submitted by Rodney Hunt. After further appraisal and investigation, the Board will probably perform future works.

Administration of IDB's was under the latest Land Drainage Act. All Boards had to undertake a complete re-valuation of land and property to bring it up to date. Constituency of Boards changed to representation related to the amount paid, with a majority of District Council representatives. The old electoral divisions were changed from the old IDB areas to three new ones, West, Central and East, which affected the number of land drainage members. However, it emphasised the importance of the protection of considerable capital investment in properties and industrial developments which had taken place in the North Level over the years. The wheel had turned on, developed areas were now providing most of the Board's income, so the ancient Land Drainage Principle still applied - those who paid the piper, called the tune.

With this new administration came a revision of byelaws set out by the Ministry with considerable consultation with IDB's: at last, contributions from developers and a planning requirement by District Councils became enforceable. We had battled for this for years with District Councils, with only a Ministry memorandum to back us up.

I remember in 1986, the Board received notice from the Planning Authority that the temporary permission for the Board's portable-building housing, Board Room and Offices, erected in 1973, would expire and not be renewed. After alternative proposals were turned down by the Planning, as the "Tank Yard" was an area of special architectural interest, the Board retained and converted the original store buildings at the end of the yard and sold the old Bedford Estate offices and the land on which the temporary building stood. It was started 1988, and officially opened 1989, by David Coates, who retired that year to be replaced by John Hoyles, whose family had a long-standing drainage pedigree. The conversion produced an office of quality, in keeping with the North Level's traditions, also preserved a building associated with the Duke of Bedford's model village of Thorney.

In my day, we were concerned about the one bridge on the main drain, the four-arched bridge at Cloughs Cross, remaining in the hands of the North Level. The County Council would not accept responsibility without considerable repair.

Since 1987, Rodney Hunt had initiated regular testing of salt-content in the Board's drains, including the main drain and South Eau. The Summer Water Distribution Scheme was operating by that time, so by 1990 it was proved that water-quality was improving, producing a complete change in the type of local flora and an increase in fish population, shown up by the triennial Water Authority fish survey. This was made possible by the level control occasioned by AFCOPS and validated our original concept. The deep water provided by the summer penning levels also reduced the amount of cott: this algae needs bright sunlight to flourish and turbidity was produced by bottom-feeding fish like carp. So when the renewal/ replacement of Cloughs Cross Bridge became necessary, and after a County Council survey had shown that the old bridge would take modern loading, and English Heritage had refused to allow demolition, it was Grade I designated. The Board made the decision to update the existing bridge and put new sluices in the recesses which housed the original sluices. The Board would be able to increase summer levels in both the South Eau and New Wryde, giving the facility to push the salt barrier even further eastwards. Repairs were commenced by contract on 1st December, 1993, 160 years after it was built. The estimated cost is £172,286, to be shared between the County Council and the Board, and it will be taken over by the County Council after completion.

We had had considerable trouble with the water-level sensor of AFCOPS. We wanted ultra-sonic sensors, but at that time they were only mains operated. However, another scientific break-through produced a 12 volt operated sensor, 20 existing sensors were changed and six more water-level records placed in the Eastern area, finally completing the installation of AFCOPS.

The schedule of financial expenditure shows amounts spent on pumping stations and pumping drains, together with 'back-up' improvements to the remaining drains over twenty years. During this period, as we all know, the RPI varied crazily, affecting the loan interest which varied from 8.35% to 15.5%. Small wonder some pumping stations cost more than others, size for size. Yet in the first thirteen years, only once did the Board's rate-increase percentage exceed the RPI, an achievement of which everybody concerned can be proud.

Out of £8.^{1}/$_4$ million, we managed to get £5.^{1}/$_4$ million grant, some £110,000 from the Common Market included, with £3.^{1}/$_4$ million paid on loan interest. With the life of the improvement estimated at 40 years, this equates to landowners paying £1.60 per acre per year, less than a sack of spuds and with no more inflationary increases. The North Level had moved into the twenty-first century.

Cloughs Cross Bridge before Renovation

Cloughs Cross Bridge from the downstream southern bank, after reconstruction

Cloughs Cross Bridge from the downstream northern bank, after reconstruction

Lincoln Sluice Gates, after reconstruction on upstream face

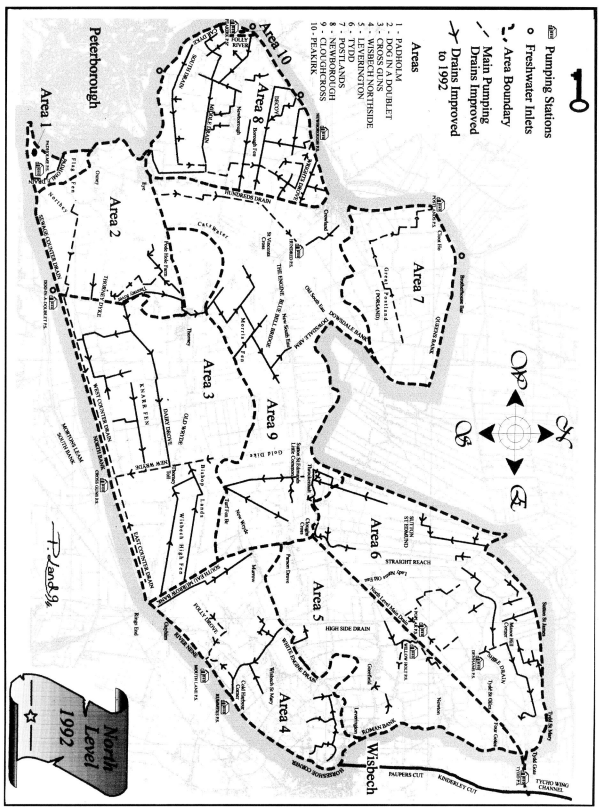

North Level in 1992

4th NORTH LEVEL MAJOR IMPROVEMENT
Total Costs 1973 - 1993

1	Padholme	157,000	None	None	157,000
2	Dog in a Doublet	833,848	214,436	194,507	1,242,791
3	Cross Guns	871,960	205,935	216,449	1,294,344
4	Wisbech Northside	300,115	None	155,954	456,069
5	Murrow	None	174,335	24,410	198,745
5, 5a	Leverington, Willow Holt	None	182,266	347,232	529,498
6, 6a 6b	Tydd, Poplars & Denhams	None	465,000	435,344	900,344
7	Postland	211,060	52,316	None	263,376
8	Newborough	311,505	32,340	544,804	888,649
9, 9a 9b	Cloughs Cross, Hundreds & Morris Fen	None	618,823	78,904	697,727
10	Peakirk	None	26,210	None	26,210
	Updating Tydd, P.S. & MR Improvements	931,000	None	None	931,000
	Main Drain Channel Stabilisation	None	214,076	None	214,076
	Water Distribution Works	None	None	238,782	260,000
	AFCOPS	220,000	None	40,000	77,565
		3,836,488	2,185,737	2,276,386	8,298,611

APPENDIX I

The Development of Field Drainage Through the Ages

The history of field drainage is as old as agriculture. The Romans were aware of the need to prevent the feet of crops becoming waterlogged.

There is considerable misunderstanding of the movement of the water table in flatland known in the Fens as the 'sock' level. There abounds a common assumption that the water level in the ditch controls the water table in the field, so at the risk of boring readers, I feel it necessary to explain the water table phenomena in more detail.

One or two simple facts:-

a)   Roots require both air and water to function, providing the soil has enough air gaps, moisture will be retained by soil particles by capillary action. It follows that roots cannot penetrate the boundary between air and water. This boundary is the Water Table.

b)   Excess water in the soil can only drain to the ditches by capillary action and like any flow, however small, must have a gradient.

c)   Capillary action can flow in all directions, including upwards, if moisture is removed from neighbouring particles by root growth during the growing season. Obviously during the growing season, usually accompanied by evaporation due to increased sun temperature, (even in the UK), the air/water boundary drops as moisture is taken up. Conversely, after the growing season when evaporation ceases, this boundary rises.

This upward and downward movement of the Water Table is only influenced by five factors:-

i) Rainfall, ii) Evaporation, iii) Transiration, *(take-up of moisture by plants)*,

iv) Capillary drainage, v) The porous nature of the soil.

The greatest effect on the water table is from the first three, and is unaffected by capillary flow through soil except in very porous conditions. Putting all this simply and destroying the common myth, the annual change of the water table level is entirely, (as a generalisation), dependent on rainfall and not the water level in the ditches and drains.

On silt/clay land this annual level variation can have a level range between 2ft to 12ft in the centre of the field, irrespective of the drain water level, but obviously there are many factors that influence this in different soil drainage characteristics and the depth of crop root systems.

You may say, in the Fen, the peatland water is kept up in the summer. This is because peat is a good conductor of water if wet. Allow it to dry out completely and it becomes impervious; water will not flow by capillary action.

Have you ever tried to water a peat mixture pot plant after being away, the water takes a long time to saturate the peat.

It is vitally important to keep the plant "feet" dry; artificial field drainage removes the surplus water in the soil and creates the right environment for the roots, ideally this should be progressive as roots penetrate, but is difficult technically. Our climate produces evaporation later in the growing life which helps.

The Romans, Saxons and mediaeval farmers strove to protect their land from flooding from the sea and rivers and tried to reduce water-logging by ploughing ridges and furrows to take off surplus rain water. Trenches filled with straw or thorn were due to carry water from the ground to the ditches, sometimes filled with shell from the sea shore - the first attempt at under-drainage. By the thirteenth century most of the farmable land was established around villages with the field and ditch system we find today, each field consisting of strip with shallow narrow "grips" leading to the ditches, a further effort to remove surplus water from the surface and an element of capillary drainage to the "grips". These fields were ploughed with the improved fixed mould board plough which moved a slice of soil instead of just loosening it.

An early treatise which dealt with field drainage was by Walter Blyth, a Captain in Cromwell's army, "The English Improver", published in 1649. He recommended that, "No man should attempt to lay out his drain by eye alone, but by aid of a true and exact water level. No drain could touch the spewing moist water unless it was a yar or 4 feet deep provided with proper outfalls." Drains should be cut straight, then filled in with "elder boughs' or stones and turfed over; there were no pipes at this time.

In 1764 Joseph Elkington discovered how to tap spring water, the bane of the upland grazier's life, marking the beginning of field investigation and under-drainage design. So famous did he become that John Johnstone was commissioned by the Board of Agriculture, in 1797, to report on his work.Johnstone reported at that time that clay pipes were being used in Essex, (probably horseshoe tiles), about 18" long x 3"-4" round. Toward the end of the eighteenth century, hand made clay tiles and bricks were in general use, designs were varied.

They progressed from 'n' shaped tiles, (like ridge tiles from which they got their name), to Horseshoe tiles with thick feet, Horseshoe with a flat plate base, and finally the round tile. In 1845, Thomas Scragg invented a machine for extruding clay tiles which reduced the price by a quarter, under-drainage was taking off.

In 1831, James Smith had published his "Remarks on Thorough Drainage and Deep Ploughing", he farmed on heavy clay land and was the first to realise the importance of soil structure, (letting air in), to water movement, (capillary action), he was the advocate of moling into piped drains.

Josiah Parks made a name for himself when he drained Chad. Moss, Lancs. He put in deep drains varying from 21' to 50' apart. His deeper drainage was, "To keep subterranean water, (water table), at a depth exceeding the power of capillary attraction to elevate it near the surface".

Controversy raged during the middle of the century regarding deep or shallow under-drains, both advocates being successful in their own environment, but not quite knowing why.

J. Bailey-Denton, (1814-1893), probably influenced the progress of under-drainage more than any other man. He farmed 400 acres in Hertfordshire and successfully created a perfectly drained holding. With the passing of 1846 Land Drainage Act he was appointed Engineer to the General Land Drainage Approvement Co which, under the Act, was empowered to supply loans for field drainage improvement and organise the work.

He was to be responsible for sponsored improvements amounting to some £1 million in the 34 years up to 1880. He had completed a survey of England and Wales in which he concluded that 15,455,000 acres needed improvement of which 7,500,000 would be "a sound and worthwhile venture". His wide experience led to acceptance by Government and learned societies as the country's leading authority on field drainage. Giving evidence to the Royal Commission on Agriculture in 1880, he estimated that some two million acres had been under-drained between 1846 and 1870.

He profoundly believed that drains should be laid at a depth of 4', but was unsure of the spacing. Aware that in free-draining soils, at this depth the spacing could be opened up, he was not so certain in heavy clay soil. However, because of the specification laid down for loans, much of the heavy land was proved to be ineffectively drained and so-called Government Drainage fell into disrepute.

In 1797, Harry Watts had devised a mole plough pulled by a team of heavy horses, or by a windlass driven by men and horses, but in 1854, John Fowler invented his steam drive apparatus. By 1855, five of a new double-engined sets steam tackle were in operation pulling in strings of clay pipes using a mole plough and had drained 10,000 acres, mostly in East Anglia, the first trenchless drainage machine.

By the end of the First World War, thousands of acres had been drained, the vast majority by hand, but although "mole" was used it became apparent that moles in unsuitable land soon collapsed - it was cheaper to tile.

Between the two world wars, the Ministry of Agriculture attempted to improve under-drainage technique, sponsoring, between 1924 and 1932, no less than 53 mole draining demonstrations as well as researching the life and hydrology of mole drains.

The Agriculture Act 1937, described as "An Act to assist farmers to increase the fertility of their land", gave powers to pay grants to Drainage Authorities which enabled them to improve main drainage and therefore, farm drainage.

The next upsurge of field drainage improvement was spawned by the onset of the 1939-45 war and the establishment of the War Agricultural Executive Committee with sweeping powers. A contract service was established commandeering both plant and men from Drainage Boards, so that by 1944, they operated 600 draglines and 300 mechanical trenchers: these were a British invention.

Farmers recognised the value of under-drainage, especially with Government grants available, the area of land being drained increased from 15,000 acres in 1944 to 105,000 in 1960. In 1958/59, exceedingly wet years, a Ministry survey, based on geological formation, concluded that 14 million acres would benefit from field drainage. This report was never published. A further Ministry survey was done in 1968/69, another extremely wet period, under more detailed headings:-

1) **Grant** - Land claimed with the help of grant since 1940 - 1.7 million acres, 6%

2) **Natural** - Free draining land - 10.5 million acres, 39%

3) **Old** - Land adequately under-drained by pre-1940 systems - 5.3 million acres 19%

4) **Improve** - Land that would benefit from artificial field drainage - 7.1 million acres 26%

5) **Out** - Land which was uneconomical to drain - 2.6 millions acres 10%

Of interest, is how much we were relying on old drainage systems in the Fens, the majority of which had been laid by hand.

At this the overall land area in cultivation was 27.3 million acres. From 1950 onwards, much work was in field trials to assess the efficacy of slotted plastic pipe. In 1962 the Ministry of Agriculture took the leading role by setting up the Field Drainage Experimental Unit, which not only produced a specification for the plastics industry, but also pioneered the development of the Trenchless Drainage Machine based on the mole plough principle.

In 1969 the Agricultural Advisory Council produced a report known as the "Strutt" report. The Council was chaired by Sir Nigel Strutt of Essex and stressed the need for continuing progress in arterial and field drainage. Grant was increased to 60% and the annual draining figure increased to 225,000 acres by 1973.

New, large trenchless machines were produced, but here and in Holland, the price of plastic pipe was more than clay pipes, but, even allowing for the huge capital cost of these machines, the work would be carried out far quicker and with less labour. Small drainage schemes were cheaper using trenchers and clay pipes, but eventually trenchless drainage and plastic pipes became the norm, the design of drainage systems was rationalised, and design manuals produced, specifications and standards implemented by the Ministry for grant aid work.

The wheel, however, turned full cycle, perfidious Government, perhaps realising the success of their policies, had reduced grant to NIL by the late seventies unless related to an overall farm improvement plan of over five years.

We all know what has happened since then. The Common Market and Brussels regulations, over production in terms of Europe's requirement, but not the rest of the world, falling commodity markets, removal of subsidies, lowering of farmers' standards, until we are now falling behind in maintaining the Drainage infra-structure plus the ever-increasing cost of maintaining and updating Arterial Drainage, without which Field Drainage is useless.

I believe that the average farm holding in the UK is some 350 acres - in 1947, it was 52 acres. This has resulted in a drift from the land of our yeoman stock which is unlikely to be replaced.

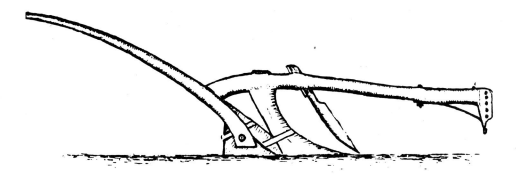

Early fixed mouldboard plough

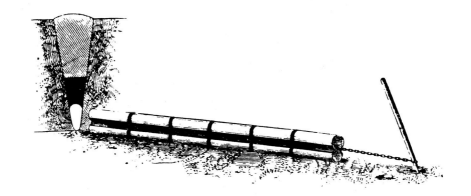

Cross section of trench & sketch of a former for 'plug' drainage

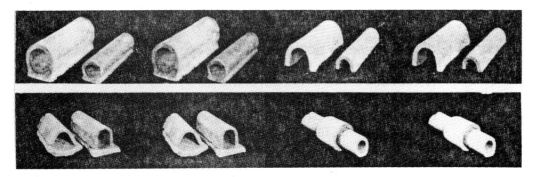

Early clay ware drains

Gt. Grandad called it 'plug drainage'

The illustration shows (a) the underground plug, to which the string of clay tiles is attached; (bb) the coulter with wheel & screw depth control at the beam; (c) beam on two pairs of wheels; (e) drain opened by hand where pipes enter the ground; (a to e) pipes under ground; (e to f) pipes above ground; (g) windlass or capstan, horse-powered; (h) wire rope from windlass to plough; (i) pulley for rope to keep plough in line.

Tile Draining by Hand:
'First Draw'

Early Tile Draining Machine.

Steam tackle mole plough.

Direct pull mole plough.

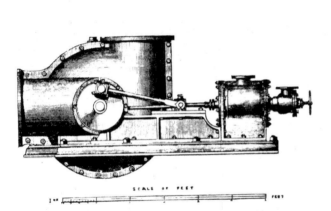

Centifugal pump by Gwynne - 1867

*Priestman cub excavator
with side-arm equipment*

APPENDIX II

Recollections & Crops in the Twentieth Century

A quote from Wentworth Day - "The Hemmants, Gees and many others are of that ancient yeoman stock, little kings on their own lands, whose roots are deeper and pedigrees longer than those of half the newly minted members of curious, latter day aristocracy".

Arthur Gee was born in 1901 and is the oldest living ex-member of the North Level. His family arrived in Thorney in 1770, to farm the Duke of Bedford's land. When the Bedford estate was sold in 1910, the Gee family bought 13 farms amounting to between 3,000 and 4,000 acres. He recalls that the farms on the estate had operated about a five-year cycle of crops, always with one third of the holding down to grass. They were not allowed to grow potatoes or mustard; cole was not allowed to seed, but only used for green fodder - one was fined if cole seeded.

They grew their first potatoes in 1911, the only crop to use artificial fertiliser, manure from the cattle stock yards. Arthur Gee recalls that sugar beet was the worst crop to grow because every operation had to be done by hand except drilling. For every 400 acres, 25 horses and 10/12 men were needed. On his holding, the Duke had underdrained 880 acres by hand.

All his land was ploughed each year by contract, using the double traction-engine method, until 1940, when he bought two diesel caterpillar-tracked tractors. He still has one which has just been rejuvenated. The first binder for cereal crops was bought during the '14/'18 War and his first combine during the '39/'45 War, (perhaps an indication of the prosperous times). his first pea-viner, a static one, was purchased in 1930, driven by a traction engine, the peas being cut and carted to the farm.

They had their own threshing tackle which was moved from farm to farm. He clearly remembered threshing-time as a lad; his job was to take the grub out to the men and chase rats with a stick.

They had a struggle during the slump, between 1922 and 1932, also the wet spring of 1937, when a lot of land went under water. He and his neighbours, the Hemmants, threatened to sue the North Level which sparked off the 'Farran' scheme.

During Arthur's life he has been a long-serving member of the Thorney Board, chairman of the North Level and Vice-chairman of the Catchment Board. He is a perfect gentleman of the old school. When I saw him in 1992, he did not object to me smoking and bought me two packets of cigarettes: one Capstan Full Strength, the other an unopened packet of Du Maurier. When I tried the Capstan, the tobacco all fell out onto the ashtray as I tapped the end. I think both packets were collector's pieces.

The Hemmant family came to Whittlesey in 1714 and William Jnr took over their present farm in 1772. He became a North Level Commissioner in 1773. A cattle and sheep man, he owned 20,000 sheep. The family bought their farms from the Duke in 1910. Jack and his brother, Arnold, were both members of the North Level, descendants of the only family who have an unbroken record of membership dating back to 1773. Jack also clearly remembers the slump, and their struggles, but they managed to buy their first tractor in 1917 and by 1930 had two, although all the work on the black land was done by horses: on 400 acres they had 25 horses and 20 men. After 1911, they grew continuous crops of potatoes, as many farms did, but this caused a proliferation of eel-worm. They first grew sugarbeet in 1923, which went to Newark by train until the Peterborough factory was built. The brothers ran a herd of Lincoln red cattle and many pigs until 1965.

Arnold still farms in Thorney with his sons and Jack is retired. He hasa phenomenal memory of Fenland families, apparently knowing everybody and their relationships. If he had followed the gee-gees he would have known every horse's pedigree.

John Clarke, from Wisbech St Mary, also remembers the depression when many farmers went broke, including large ones. The smaller farms were kept afloat by the wife's poultry enterprise. Until about

1935, wheat was fetching £5.5s. per ton and compound poultry feed was £4.5s. Public school fees were £30 per term and inflation negligible. Potatoes brought £50 per ton in 1938, riddled, bagged and loaded. Some of the best land in Wisbech St Mary was offered for sale and withdrawn for want of a bid of £28 per acre. They had 175 acres under cultivation, 21 in orchard and 54 in grass, operated by twelve men, and five or six working horses with five to six to break in, work or sell, fetching £60 to £130 each.

Tractors were used for all the ploughing after 1936, but horses were still used for hoeing, wheat, beet-lifting and carting and harrowing until after the '39-'45 war, but with breaking up of grassland, horses and cattle in the North Level diminished rapidly in the early 50's.

1935 onwards, tractors were more prevalent; binders were fitted with hitches, and the tractor and binder did not pull up when the going got tough. The best early tractor was the Farmall. The Clarkes had their first tractor, a Triton, only used for belt-grinding and hauling, too heavy for the land. They had their first combine in 1944, a Minneapolis Moline, English made, and poor larger farmers had the Massey Ferguson 21, an excellent machine, as John commented. Many bags of King Edward potatoes and braces of pheasant found their way to the lady in the Ministry of Agriculture in London, who dealt with the allocation of imported farm machinery.

Growing beet was a tedious business, drilling on a finely prepared bed, hand-hoeing, singling, lifting, pulling, topping, rowing, heaping into carts, moving to the roadside and subsequently loading into lorries. In the early days it was loaded into rail trucks to go to Peterborough. John built his first cold store for fruit in 1950 and his grain store in 1955, holding 100 tons and 425 tons respectively.

John was on the Wisbech Northside Board for many years and held the title of Dyke Reeve, later called the Officer, who supervised all the work. He is still a serving member of the North Level IDB and was a member of the WNRA.

When I asked John Clarke about the development of mechanical farming and to pick out the most important, without hesitation he said, "The Ferguson 3-point linkage and hydraulic hitch." When I asked, why, he said, "Because it didn't kick or tread on your foot!"

Henry Shippey is the senior member of that well-known Cambridgeshire cricketing family from Newton. His father grew a fairly large acreage of strawberries. They moved to the present farm in 1905. Henry went to Newton village school from 1922-28, then started work. He recalls that all the school holidays were tied to fruit and potato harvest time. He wondered what people would think today if they knew that apple trees were sprayed six times a year with a nicotine/arsenate of lead mixture, which he used until 1939. The Bramley orchard was planted in 1900 directly from stock from the original Bramley tree in Newark, which is still there; he has one still in the orchard. The Isle of Ely Research Centre in Barton Road, Wisbech, with which Henry was involved, and which started in 1920, investigated methods of dealing with pests, etc. He was also chairman of the Wisbech and District Fruit Growers Association, formed in 1901, as well as a member of the NFU formed in 1969.

He farmed 300 acres, of which 50 were hard fruit and 60 of grass, broken up in 1916, and recalls that between 1920 and 1930 they dug 50 acres by hand each year, and during the last war laid down 49 acres of underdrains, also by hand. He thought that the breakthrough in fruit-tree technology came with the development of the East Morling Research Establishment in 1920, which developed root stock to grow trees to controlled heights and resistant to many diseases.

Henry followed his father's tradition of strawberry growing until 1938. He grew two or three varieties, often self-propagating, with a yield of $1^1/_2$ tons per acre. Before tractors, he employed 50 men and 22 horses, taking his first pea-crop to Smedley's viner in 1925, the whole vine cut and loaded on carts. There was a queue past the Leverington turning to Sutton Road, Wisbech.

When talking to seedsmen Sid Gott and John Reeve, I discovered some interesting facts about Fen crops: how sugarbeet was developed in Germany, arriving here in the 1920's. The single seed monogerm was not developed until 1948. The crop was lifted by hand until 1930, when the first mechanical lifter appeared; the automatic Whitsed beet-harvester materialised in 1950.

Cereals were first grown by hand-broadcasting, but the crop could not be weeded, the first drill appearing in the eighteenth century. Hand-broadcasting was first followed by the fiddle sower which could measure the seed accurately. The advent of row-drilling meant that the crop could be hoed by hand to get rid of weeds and therefore increase the yield.

Harvesting progressed from cutting with a scythe or sickle to a horse-pulled reaper in 1851, to the binder in 1878, this being in use until the first combines after the War. Threshing progressed from beating and tossing with a flail to the steam threshing machine in 1840, to tractor-driven threshing machines to combines.

"Yeoman" seed was virtually the only seed available, one winter and two spring varieties: it was long-strawed, much-loved by thatchers, but stood very badly. Some new varieties were produced , but there were no royalties to encourage plant-breeders. They had to charge more for their developed seed so were reluctant. This situation remained until the Seeds Royalty Act of 1964. However, a French seed, Capelle, was imported at the end of the 1939-45 war and was popular from 1950 to 1976, when new varieties were arriving from the National Seed Development Organisation, (Breeders), set up in 1970. This organisation must be one of the greatest agricultural developments in post-war Britain. The breeding success has doubled the farmers' yield, increased disease resistance, shortened the straw so that it remains standing under severe conditions, all because farmers did not want to increase the price of seed by royalties. Obviously some of the increase of yield was also due to fertiliser development, but now they find they don't need so much!!

Since 1931, most wheat was dressed with mercury-based chemicals to control "Bunt", this was banned in 1992.

GLOSSARY OF LAND DRAINAGE TERMS

ACCRETION	The natural build up of material on sea-shore or river by deposition of silt and suspension. By custom, land which builds up on the sea-shore belongs to the frontage, if the land so added is above the level of High Water Ordinary Spring Tides. Land accreted below this level is Crown land.
ACRE SHOT	Annual or special drainage rate collected by the Dyke-Reeve of each Parish or sub-district.
ADZE	A type of axe with the cutting edge at right angles to the shaft. Used for pointing poles, grubbing out roots and originally for hollowing out tree trunks to make boats.
AEGER OR BORE	The first wave of a tide coming up a river. Probably derived from AE gir the name of the Norse Ocean God or from Egar the Saxon word for ocean.
ARCHIMEDEAN SCREW	A form of pump of ancient origin, used for raising water by an inclined tube in which a large screw on a long shaft rotates. Known in Cambridgeshire as a Poly Ann.
ARTERIAL DRAIN	A primary water-course taking water from smaller ditches to the main outfall or pumping station.
AXIAL FLOW PUMP	A low lift land-drainage pump with an impellor driven by a verticle shaft. The water flows parallel to the axis of the pump, hence axial flow.
AYSE OR AISE	To ease or lift. A man is said to ayse water out of a ditch when it has been held up by a dam for cleaning out purposes. Also owse, and houst.
BACK TIP	A wooden, comma usually oak, longhandled spade tipped with metal used to throw mud from a deep dyke. Also tip tool or snotty nose.
BALL DI**NGER**	Single pole for piling with a hammer ringed round the pole.
BANK REEVE	Official responsible to Dyke Reeve for maintenance of a length of sea bank.
BARROW ROAD	A plank roadway for wheeling clay barrows up out of the drain during excavation work, often pulled by ponies.
BATTER	The sloping side of a waterway or bank. Battering is the act of forming the sloping side.
BEAR BOWL	A bowl shaped wooden shovel for very wet mud.
BEAR'S MUCK	A peat like material consisting of a mixture of vegetable matter and clay having a fetid smell and found in parts of the fens. Generally the decaying roots and stalks of phragmites.
BECKET	A peat cutting knife.
BED	The bottom of a water course.
BERM	A flat area in embankment often used for access or to increase flood storage.
BILL HOOK	Short handled tool for cutting weed undergrowth, long handled version called a slasher.
BIRD TIDES	The tides in early summer that are generally lower than at other times and allow the seabirds to hatch their young on the saltmarshes.
BISCOT, TRISCOT AND WOPENY	Varying degrees of misdemeanor attracting fines by the Commissioners of Sewers and collected by the Dyke Reeves.
BITTER HINGLES	Snares to catch Bitterns.

BLANKET WEED OR COTT	Floating weed like algae with cottonwool texture and resembling thick moss, grows abundantly in the fen drains and is difficult to remove.
BLOW UP	A term applied to the bursting of water through a bank or sluice.
BOVATE OR OX GANG	The quanitity of land that a pair of oxen could keep in husbandry. Usually about 15 acres, but varies according to the conditions of the land. Eight bovates made one carucate.
BOX HORSE	A box shaped stand of varying dimensions with diagonal bracings used in the same way as a trestle, but more suitable on soft ground.
BREECH	A bust in the bank.
BREED OR RETCH	A measure of land. The strip an implement works in one pass.
BREEDLINGS	Dwellers in the fens.
BRINK OR BRAY	The point at which the sloping bank of a water-course becomes horizontal at land level. See prick.
BRUSHING	See roding.
BUMBLES	Reeds used for making chair seats.
BUND	Bund wall or ring earthwork to protect a weak section of sea or river bank.
BYELAW	Special tax levied in time of great need, ie a great breach.
CARUCATE	Carve or plough land. A measure of land varying according to quality equal to eight ox gangs or about 120 acres. As much land as may be tilled and laboured with one plough, and the beast belonging to it, in one year. Also as much as was sufficient for one family.
CATCHMENT	Area of land, the surface from which drains to one drainage system or outfall.
CAULKING	Driving small stones between dressed stone to secure them.
CESS	Margin or foreland, the space between the foot of the bank and the channel. The land adjacent to a drain on which the drainage authority has a right to deposit spoil and over which it has right of access. The width was sometimes laid down by statute.
CHAIN	The imperial unity of length - 22 yards. It was the most commonly used measurement for water courses, embankments and land drains. Still in use for piece work letting. No suitable metric equivalent.
CILL OR SILL	Usually the hard wood base on which stop boards or sluice gates fit.
CLAPPER	Flat valve automatically shut by the tide or floodwater.
CLAY CORE	Puddled clay centre of sea or river banks or of dams to resist seepage.
CLEANSE	Term used for cleaning water courses of silt and weeds.
CLOOT	A door or dam for stopping water backing up a drain.
CLOUGH OR CLOW	A sluice with doors which when opened allow the interior water to run out and when closed prevent river or sea water from entering.
CLOUGHERS	Sods of earth used for cradging, also known as sads.
COFFER DAM	A dam of sheet piles driven around an area to form a sealed and strengthened box which can be dewatered by pumping so that work can be done within.
COTT	See Blanket Weed.
COUNTER DRAIN	A drain running parallel with or counter to another drain or river.

CRADGE	A small temporary bank. Throwing up earth on top of a bank to fill up low places and raise it temporarily to prevent water flowing over.
CREEPER	A spiked metal gripper strapped to the boots for barrow road walking.
CREST	The top level of sea defence, flood, flood banks or weirs.
CROCKER	Strong steel or iron spade for hand excavation work.
CROFT	Enclosed land on the borders of a stream.
CROME, CROOME OR CRORME	A long handled tool with a flat blade at right angles to the shaft for cleaning out culverts. Also a four tined fork with tines bent at right angles.
CULVERT	Piping to form crossing of a drain. See stow way.
CUT OR CUTT	New or realigned water course.
DANEGELT	A land tax of two shillings on every carucate of land, levy to raise money to defend East Anglia against the Danes.
DELPH, DELF OR DELFT	Saxon for a ditch, frequently applied to a drain running parellel with and at the foot of a bank.
DRIFT ROAD OR DROVE	A wide road with grass side suitable for driving cattle.
DUMMY	A shirtlike smock, usually white, worn by toolmen to stop their clothes getting splashed with mud. Sometimes it was a rule that if a man appeared for work on a Monday without a clean dummy he was fined a penny which went into the beer kitty.
DYKE	The ancient English term for a bank protecting land from inundation. In Holland banks are still called Diyks. Gradually the term came to be applied to the hollow made by digging out the spoil to make the bank and then gradually to all small drains and ditches. In Dugdale, the term is applied to both banks and drains. It is equivalent to the Latin 'fossa' a combination of ditch and bank, and it is derived from the Danish dige.
DYKE REEVE	An officer appointed by the Court of Sewers for every Parish in the fens to look after the banks, sewers and water courses and collect the sewers or Dyke Reeve rate. The word Reeve means a bailiff or officer.
EA	The Saxon for an island or land surrounded by water. Village names ending in an ea or ey denote islands, eg Thorney, Manea.
EAU, OR EA	A drain from the Scandinavian Aa, water. An old fenman always pronounces it 'ea' which no doubt is correct.
EELHIVE	A wicker or wire net eel trap.
FAGGOTING	The use of bundles of small branches and twigs, usually hawthorn or willow as a protection against slipping or scouring in silt batters. Also used as the foundations for stone training walls in tidal in tidal outfall chambers. Locally a faggot and kid are identical. A standard faggot is a yard long and a yard round.
FASCINE	A long faggot bound together with twine or willow to form a mattress for bank and bed protection and on foundations for stone training banks. Fascine work has become to mean the general use of all types of faggots and kids.
FENNIFERS	Officers appointed to see that fish were not taken from certain meres and rivers in the Bedford Level at improper season.
FEN NIGHTINGALE	A frog.
FEN SLODGER	A man who gained his living from the fen by wild-fowling and reed-cutting.

FEN TIGER	A fen dweller probably derived from the Celtic Tiak, a ploughman.
FISH GARTH	A cage for catching fish or places fenced off at the sides of a river, frequently mentioned in Court of Sewers records as an obstruction in a water course.
FLAP VALVE	Sluice valve normally automatic, which allows one way flow only. Closes on the rise of the tide or river level and opens to discharge water on fall. Doors made be top or side hung. Also a clapper.
FLOOD PLAIN	Natural valley of a rive over which floods will spread if not controlled.
FOOT IRON	A metal plate strapped to the sole of a boot to prevent wear when digging with a spade.
FRANKIE	Heron, from its call "frank".
FREEBOARD	Vertical distance between peak flood level and the top of an embankment or between land level and the level of water in the water course.
GAD	A measuring pole generally ten foot in length, also an eel spear.
GAT, GATE OR GUT	A road or way, an opening or entrance, also applied to channels leading from an estuary to a river sluice or harbour thus Boston Gat in the Wash and sluice gut.
GAUGE OR GOUGE	A narrow iron or steel spade for cutting narrow trenches for tile drains.
GOULT OR GALT	Hard, blue clay. Galting is the covering of peatland with clay.
GLEEVE OR PILGRE	Forks to catch eels. The former has flat prongs, the latter round prongs.
GORE	A weir, an obstruction in the water course.
GOTE, GAUT OR GOWT	A Saxon term for a sluice, usually between fresh and salt water. Saxon, Geotan - to pour out, eg Tidgote, or Guthram Gowt.
GRAFT	Very hard work.
GRAFTING TOOL	A ditch digging shovel.
GRAVEL FORK	A heavy iron, two-pronged fork for breaking out hard, ironbound gravel from a drain bed.
GULL OR GRUNDGOTE	A hole made by water reaching a bank.
HAFFS	Turves of coarse grass "that the river be rodded, hooked, haffed, scoured and cleaned" - order of Court of Sewers 1616.
HASSOCKS	Turves of coarse grass. The Gozzards (goose herds) used to get across the fen "by jumping from hassock to hassock". Owners of land in the Bedford Level were entitled to have their land hassocked by the Scotch prisoners at six shilling per acre.
HICKING BARROW	A wooden stretcher for carting turves.
HODDING SPADE	A heart-shaped iron spade for cutting large squares of turf, or the batter of a drain.
HOLT	Wood or land covered in brush.
HOOKING	Cutting weeds at the side of a drain with a hook or sickle.
HUNDRED	A division of the county. In Saxon times, the county was divided into companies of a hundred families under a chief.
HYRNE OR HURN	A nook or angle. A corner of land bounded by water courses. A corner of a Parish, eg Guyhurn and Holbeach Hurn.

INING OR INNING	Abbreviation of 'enclosing' in relation to reclamation of land or fitters.
INNAM	Land taken into cultivation.
JACK BALLING	Double handling where spoil has to be moved beyond the reach of one person or machine in two concerted operations.
KNOT	A seabird, formerly very common on the saltmarshes, named after the Danish King Canute, or Canut. They were first imported especially for his eating.
LANDED UP	The filling up of a drain or river with weeds and silt.
LEEK	To drain by throwing water out with a wooden shovel or leek bowl.
LEVEL	A drainage district or lowland area of a river valley or fen capable of being managed as one unit, being land of similar drainage characteristics, eg North Level.
LODE	A fen drain.
LOPING POLE	A pole used for jumping over fen dykes.
MERE OR MEER	A fen lake.
MOLE	A circular molelike tunnel formed in subsoil by deep ploughing with the mole plough usually confined to clay soils.
MONKEY OR TUP	Pile driving drop hammer.
PADDLES	The boards or scoops of a pumping wheel, also the doors of a sluice which can be drawn up to let out water.
PENSTOCK	Sluice door used for shutting off or regulating flow, capable of being wound, shut, open mechanically or manually.
PINTOL	A large pin on which a sluice gate sits and swings.
PINTOL POT	Housing at the base of the quoin to receive the pintol.
PITCHING	Placing stones on slopes of the river channel as lining to prevent scour.
PODE	A frog.
POLING BOARDS	Short boards with walings as a coffer dam.
PRICK	A point where the channel slope (batter) starts, ie the top of the batter. To prick out is to mark out the batter line of a new cut.
PUDDLED CLAY	Brick clay moistened and trodden down with bare feet.
REVETMENT	Protection with hard material of a river bank, embankment for sea bank against scour.
RHYNE	A drain in Somerset.
RINGING FRAME	A timber pole frame with hand rope over a pulley attached to a drop hammer (tup). The hand rope, or bell rope, would have up to six tassels or cats to permit six men to pull on the rope.
RODDON	Simulous silt ridges on the land surface which were originally silt filled tidal creeks which form ridges as the surrounding peat shrinks.
RODDING OR RODING	The cutting and clearing away of reeds in the drain.
RUN-OFF	Water running off a catchment area to a water course. A major factor in calculations for channel desing.

SADS	Sods of earth for cradging, also cloughers.
SASSE	A sluice with doors for keeping out the tides. Frequently used in early proceedings of the Bedford Level.
SCOOP	A narrow tool for crumbing up the bottom on a tile drain trench.
SCOUR	Natural wearing away of earth banks by high velocity flows. Scouring out is flushing mud from channels by sudden release of water.
SCUTTLE, OR LINCOLNSHIRE PUMP	A tin bath with rope harness worked by two men. Could move 500 gallons per hour.
SEVERALS	Private land, not common.
SEWER	Old term, still used, for main drain maintained by the Internal Drainage Board.
SHEARS OR SNICKLES	Flat scythelike blades strung together and pulled along a drain from both banks to cut weeds. Handles called paddlehooks.
SLACKER	The drain door of the inside of a tidal sluice used for regulating the height of water in the drains. Now means any structure for regulating water flow.
SLATTERY	Rainy, specially applied to showery weather.
SLIPE OR SLAMP	A narrow strip of land between two drains.
SLUFF OR SLOUGH	A large bladed wooden shovel for wet mud.
SOCK OR SOAK	The level at which underground water stands in the subsoil. Varies in accordance with the wetness or dryness of the season.
SPIT	A spadedepth.
STAUNCH OR STOCK	A weir or dam with wooden door to regulate flow. Often made of wood and in appearance like the punishment stock.
STOWWAY	Passage from one field to another - pipes or wooden trunk.
STUNT	Blunt of manner, steep.
TOE	The bottom of a bank or batter.
TRAINING WORKS	Stone banks built in the river estuary to increase the velocity in order to scour the bed.
TURBURY	Peat cutting for burning.
WAINBRIDGE	Bridge wide enough for farm waggons.
WAKES	Holes in the ice.
WAILING	Longitudinal member, steel or timber, supporting vertical piling or revetment.
WARP	Alluvial deposit left by the tide.
WASHLAND	Land beside a river reserved for storage of floodwater by overspill, eg Cowbit Wash, Wittlesey Wash.
WATER TABLE	See sock level.
WRACK OR WRECK	Weeds and floating rubbish carried about by the tides and deposited on the shore.

LIST OF FURTHER ACCOUNTS OF THE FENS

LABELYE C. (ENGINEER) The result of a view of the Great Level of the Fens in July 1745. Printed by George Woodfall at the King's Arms, Nr Craggs Court, Charing Cross.

KINDERLY N. (ENGINEER) The Ancient and Present state of the Navigation of the towns of Lynn, Wisbech and Boston. Printed by J. Noon at the White Hart in the Poulty MDCCLI.

ELSTOB W. (ENGINEER) An historical account of the Great Level of the Fens, called the Bedford Level and other fens and marshes. Printed by W. Wittingham at Lynn in MDCCXCIII.

DUGDALE W. The History of imbanking and draining of divers fens and marshes in foreign parts and in this kingdom and improvements thereby. Printed in London by W. Bowyer and J. Nichols MDCCLXXII.

MILLAR S.H. & SKERTCHLEY S.B.J. Fenland Past and Present. Published in 1878

JOHNSTONE J. The Mode of Draining Land. Published in 1801

HUTCHINGSON H. Practical Draining of Land. Published in 1844.

DARBY H.C. The Medieval Fens. Changing Fenland. Published by Cambridge University Press in 1974 and 1983.

NICHOLSEN H.H. Principals of Field Drainage. Published in 1940 and 1953.

WENTWORTH DAY J. A History of the Fens. Published by G. Harrop in 1954.

WELLS S. A collection of laws which form the constitution of the Bedford Level Corporation. Published by R. Pheney, 17 Fleet Street, in 1828

PRIOR F. The Book of Flag Fen Prehistoric Fenland Centre. Published by B. J. Butford/English Heritage in 1985.

CLARK E.F. George Barker Bidder, the Calculating Boy. Published by K.S.L. Publications, Bedford.

HILLS R.L. Machines, Mills and Unaccountable Costly Necessities. Published by Gooze & Sons, Norwich.

GRIEVE H. The Great Tide. Published by the County Council of Essex in 1959.

STOREY E. Spirit of the Fens. Portrait of the Fen Country, The Solitary Landscape. Call a Summer Country. The Winter Fens. Published by Robert Hale, London.

WATSON W. The history of the ancient town and port of Wisbech. Published in 1827.

GOODWIN SIR H. Fenland, Its Ancient Past and Uncertain Future. Published by Cambridge University Press in 1978.

REGAL TABLE FROM 1066

1066 - 1087	William the Conquerer I		1558 - 1603	Elizabeth I
1087 - 1100	William Rufus II		1603 - 1625	James I
1100 - 1135	Henry I		1925 - 1649	Charles I
1135 - 1154	Stephen		1649 - 1660	Cromwell - *Commonwealth of England*
1154 - 1189	Henry II		1660 - 1685	Charles II
1189 - 1199	Richard I		1685 - 1689	James II
1199 - 1216	John		1689 - 1694	William & Mary
1216 - 1272	Henry III		1694 - 1702	William III
1272 - 1307	Edward I		1702 - 1714	Anne
1307 - 1327	Edward II		1714 - 1727	George I
1327 - 1377	Edward III		1727 - 1760	George II
1377 - 1399	Richard II		1760 - 1819	George III
1399 - 1413	Henry IV		1819 - 1830	George IV
1413 - 1422	Henry V		1830 - 1837	William IV
1422 - 1461	Henry VI		1837 - 1901	Victoria
1461 - 1483	Edward IV		1901 - 1910	Edward VII
1483 -	Edward V		1910 - 1936	George V
1483 - 1485	Richard III		1936	Edward VIII
1485 - 1509	Henry VII		1936- 1952	George VI
1509 - 1547	Henry VIII		1952 -	Elizabeth II
1547 - 1553	Edward VI			
1553 - 1558	Mary			